A Candlelight Ecstasy Romance®

SHE STRUGGLED FOR A MOMENT,
HER FURY MAKING HER WILD. . . .
Then she realized she was where she wanted to be,
in his arms. She stopped struggling and let the sensations of wild excitement tingle through her.

"Ross," she murmured, burying her head in his
shoulder. "Oh, Ross."

She lay there with his hard body against the softness
of hers, suddenly aware that he was as disturbed as
she was. His hands played over her, making her body
sing with a wilder music than she had dreamed possible. She moaned and twisted, caught between wanting his hands to orchestrate this melody forever
. . . and aching for the crescendo to begin that would
make her his.

CANDLELIGHT ECSTASY ROMANCES ®

WILD RHAPSODY

Shirley Hart

A CANDLELIGHT ECSTASY ROMANCE ®

Published by
Dell Publishing Co., Inc.
1 Dag Hammarskjold Plaza
New York, New York 10017

ISBN: 0–440–19545–4

Printed in the United States of America
First printing—March 1983

To Our Readers:

We have been delighted with your enthusiastic response to Candlelight Ecstasy Romances®, and we thank you for the interest you have shown in this exciting series.

In the upcoming months we will continue to present the distinctive sensuous love stories you have come to expect only from Ecstasy. We look forward to bringing you many more books from your favorite authors and also the very finest work from new authors of contemporary romantic fiction.

As always, we are striving to present the unique absorbing love stories that you enjoy most—books that are more than ordinary romance.

Your suggestions and comments are always welcome. Please write to us at the address below.

Sincerely,

The Editors
Candlelight Romances
1 Dag Hammarskjold Plaza
New York, New York 10017

CHAPTER ONE

It was the smell that triggered the memory, the heavy, earthy smell of just-watered plants.

It was morning, and the dining room had every appearance of normality, the round glass table set for two and the winter sun sparkling on the snow outside, but to Anne Runford it was a summer afternoon, and she was seventeen, standing on the dock, waving excitedly to two men, her heart beating in a strange thumping rhythm at the sight of the younger one, who rowed the small boat with smooth motions of his muscular arms. . . .

Anne clung to the door for a moment, fighting the memory, her long, slender fingers clutching the smooth woodwork, grasping the familiar grooves for comfort.

She told herself she was being ridiculous to think about something that had happened so long ago. It had been ten years between that afternoon and this morning, and during those years she had almost succeeded in wiping the events of that summer out of her mind.

But now, once started, the memories went on. In her mind's eyes she could see his lithe body moving out of the boat. . . . She clamped down on her thoughts and walked to the table to pull back a chair, only to be taunted by another memory as a leaf brushed her elbow. A leaf had touched her bare arm that afternoon, too, as she had come out of the trees and helped the two men dock the boat. . . .

She could not allow the memory to continue. Her left hand shook as she picked up the morning paper, and the diamond engagement ring was an unwelcome weight on her hand. Was she really going to marry Michael . . . and risk trusting someone again? *Yes, you are,* she told herself severely. *Now, stop condemning yourself. That was years ago. You won't make that kind of mistake again.* . . .

Grace appeared in her unobtrusive way and asked, "Coffee, Anne?"

She put the paper aside and said, "Yes, please, Grace." Determined to keep her mind on the present, she glanced up and smiled at the housekeeper. "Nice to see the sunshine this morning."

Grace nodded sagely. "Winter's not through with us yet, you can be sure of that."

"But somehow it doesn't look as cold if the sun is shining," Anne countered. She reached for the paper again, but a sound at the doorway stopped her. Shari stood there with a very uncharacteristic frown wrinkling her brow. Her sister, at sixteen, with her slim figure and dark curls, could have very little to worry about, Anne thought as the girl moved gracefully into the room. She was ready for school, wearing a roll-collar sweater in a flattering lavender color, and a long, swishy wool skirt in shades of matching plaid. She settled into a chair beside Anne and wrinkled her nose. Anne wondered if she, too, smelled the plants. Shari's perfume mingled with their hothouse fragrance as she picked up her napkin.

"Those plants smell gross," Shari said, eyeing her glass of juice. "I don't know how Daddy expects us to eat with them practically surrounding us. I have nightmares that someday one is going to pounce and make a snack out of me."

10

Anne smiled. "Just be glad Mother wasn't fond of Venus's-flytraps."

"Well, I still don't see why Daddy keeps them. Just because they used to belong to Mother. She didn't care what happened to them . . . any more than she cared what happened to us . . ." Anne's brows flew up, and Shari's voice trailed off.

There was a quiet in the room that seemed to stretch for several minutes. Then Anne asked easily, "Want part of the paper?"

Those clear eyes, which hesitated between hazel and green, flickered over her. "You haven't looked at it yet?" Shari toyed nervously with her fork, letting it teeter back and forth against the glass table to produce a series of repetitious, increasingly annoying clicks.

"Not yet." The clicks went on relentlessly, and Anne gritted her teeth. "Shari, would you please stop that?"

Her sister was instantly contrite. "I'm sorry."

"Do you have a test today?"

Shari lifted her shoulders in an elegantly casual shrug. "No."

"Then what is wrong with you?"

"Nothing," the younger girl said, but her eyes darted to the folded paper, and Anne, after years of trying to outguess her younger sister, knew with an instinctive turn of mind that there was something in the paper that was making Shari nervous.

"All right," Anne said, leaning back in her chair as Grace came in with the steaming plates of scrambled eggs and toast. "Out with it."

Shari shot a quick glance at Grace, whose stoic face was no help at all.

"I think Daddy's wrong," she burst out when Grace had gone back into the kitchen. She leaned forward and helped herself to the golden eggs that were on the plate between them. "I don't think you should have to read it in the paper."

"Read what in the paper?" For the second time Anne reached

for the folded sheaf lying near her plate. Shari's small hand came out and covered hers.

There was a silence, as if Shari were gathering her breath. Then she said softly, "That Dad is selling the glassworks."

Anne's body seemed to contract, as if she had received a harsh blow. "Selling the glassworks?"

Shari's hand tightened on hers. "It's been announced to the press and it's to be in today's paper."

There was the shock of knowing that her father was, for some reason, selling a business and a craft that had been connected with the Runford name for years, but there was the added shock of knowing that no one had seen fit to confide in her.

"Why didn't he tell me?"

"Oh, Anne, you know why he didn't tell you. He knows you have a—a thing for the business. He kept thinking something might fall through, and he didn't want to tell you when it was just in the negotiation stages. Then when everything went through and he knew he had to tell you, he—lost his nerve, I think."

She felt betrayed. That Shari, who rarely went down to the glassworks and cared nothing for the beauty that was created there daily, was the one to be telling her this was astounding in itself, but even worse, the fact that her father had said nothing at all to her hurt.

"Is everything—settled?" Anne asked, a foolish ache inside her making her refuse to believe the sale was a fait accompli.

"Of course," Shari said airily. "You don't think Dad would breathe a word to the press until the transaction was complete, do you? Rumors have been flying for months at the plant, but Daddy has been noncommittal—until last night. That's when he talked to the reporters. He was going to wait up for you, but I knew he hadn't when I saw your face." She looked down at her plate and picked up a bit of toast. "Some of the employees are worried because Western Data Systems is a California-based

12

conglomerate, but Daddy assured them they didn't have anything to worry about—"

Anne felt the blood leave her face. "Western Data Systems?"

"The company that purchased the glassworks," Shari said, her white teeth biting into the toast.

"Carson Leyton's company?"

Shari gave her a sharp look. "Yes, that's the one. How did you know the name?"

She fought to control her voice. "The Leyton family had a cottage not far from ours up in the Thousand Islands. We used to—know them quite well," she said, marveling that she could be sitting here saying these things to her sister. "I suppose you were too young to remember."

Shari frowned. "I must have been. I don't remember going up to the Islands at all."

"You were very young when we stopped going." To change the subject, she said, "Are you drinking coffee this morning?"

"No." Shari glanced at her watch. "Oh, my gosh. I've got to go or I'll miss the bus." She hurled herself out of the chair and came around the table to press a quick kiss on her sister's cheek. "Don't worry, Anne. After all, in six months you'll be an old married woman. What will you care about a stupid old glassworks then, anyway? Bye."

Tugging on a white bulky coat, she picked up her books from the chair beside the door and ran out, trailing the scent of good perfume, her sage philosophy still lingering in Anne's ears.

The door slammed and, as if that were her cue, Grace appeared. "Don't know why that girl can't allow a few more minutes of time," the housekeeper mumbled. "She never eats a complete meal."

Anne lifted her cup of coffee to lips that were curved in a slight smile. "That's part of her charm."

"Umph. Seems to me she might take a leaf from your book." Grace's eyes moved approvingly over the sleek black suit Anne wore with a ruffled, feminine blouse. Her tawny hair was caught

13

neatly at a clasp at the nape of her neck. "You never seem to have any trouble getting ready on time. You've always been the sensible one . . . teaching at your music school and all—"

The click of Anne's cup against the glass table stopped the housekeeper's discourse. "I won't be in for dinner this evening," she said, her voice cool. "Michael and I are going out."

Her crisp uniform rustling as she walked around the table, Grace gave an equally cool nod. "High time, I'd say. You've been working too hard. You need some time to play, too, you know. Never had to tell you that when you were little," she grumbled as she picked up the plates. "It wasn't till after you turned eighteen you got so career minded."

A flash of pain seared Anne. Her mobile face betrayed her for only a moment. Her mouth was controlled when she reached for the paper and Grace had rounded the table enough to look up at her.

Even those disturbing headlines were less painful to contemplate than her seventeenth summer. RUNFORD PLANT TO BE SOLD, and below it in smaller type, "New owner insists no jobs will be lost." "Did you know about this?" She glanced up at Grace, and then unfolded the paper, only to be electrified by the sudden glimpse of the picture that accompanied the article. The photographer had captured her father, smiling and shaking hands with a dark-haired man shown in profile. But the side view was enough to show the lean body in a well-tailored suit, the broad shoulders, the taut jaw, and the head of black hair that was full around the well-shaped head.

Anne caught her breath, the small inward catch almost inaudible. The housekeeper heard it and shook her head, misinterpreting the little sound of shock. "Yes, I knew, and I think it's a good thing, too." Laden with dishes, nodding and muttering to herself, the woman went out of the room, leaving Anne to stare at the photograph that had jumped off the page and punched the air from her lungs.

* * *

Ross Leyton, Carson Leyton's son and representative of Western Data Systems, flew into Runford by private plane Sunday to act as liaison between his father's conglomerate and Runford Glass. Leyton told reporters in this city today that there would be no significant changes in the operation of the glassworks and that Western's involvement with Runford would be focused on increased advertising of glass products.

Just seeing his name in print was enough to jar her already unsteady nerves. But she forced her eyes to follow the words down the page.

"We know Runford profits are down," Leyton said candidly in a private interview, "but we believe there is a place for the work of talented craftsman in today's technological world. Western wants to ensure that the gaffer doesn't become an extinct species."

She threw down the paper and shoved it away from her with an extraordinary violence. What would Ross Leyton know about a gaffer, the father-master of glassblowing?

The breakfast that Grace had prepared seemed suddenly tasteless. She folded her napkin, laid it beside her plate, and rose, tugging the skirt of her dark suit away from the velvet cushion, where it clung. There had been a velvet cushion that night, too, but she had not been wearing a skirt. . . .

She quickened her steps and almost ran up the curving oak stairs. Inside her room, she snatched her music bag up from her bed and pulled her coat from the closet. She couldn't give in to her thoughts. She had come to terms with the past long ago. She couldn't let it rise up to haunt her now, not when she had finally overcome her deepest fear and agreed to marry Michael. She would be his wife, and continue her work as the head of the piano department at Runford Music School. Her future was planned—safe.

But she caught a glimpse of herself in the mirror and wondered where that sedate, controlled woman Grace had admired only moments ago had gone. Her tall, slim body was tense with nerves, and her pale skin was flushed, a vivid contrast to her dark jacket. She tossed the coat and books back down on the bed and went to her dresser. Releasing her tawny hair from its clasp, she combed it and brushed it into submission. The familiar, almost golden eyes stared back at her from the mirror. They were sensual cat eyes, eyes that betrayed that deep core of sensuality within her. *You can hide everything else—hide your feminine body, hide your long hair—but you can't hide those eyes that once hungered for one man's love so much that you—* Furiously she caught her hair back into the turquoise clip and buttoned the jacket of her suit to the top of her throat. Unbidden came the thought that even her suit couldn't hide her femininity, that her curves were the full, mature curves of a woman now and not those of a teenage girl.

She twisted away from the mirror and walked down the stairs, purposely forcing her mind to focus on her surroundings the way she had learned to do years ago. She looked down at the living room with an aching pleasure. She had chosen the shades of deep blue and turquoise to provide the background for the free-form glass pitcher that sat in splendor on a low glass table. She had also been the one to place the glass sculpture of a Greek discus thrower, his body twisted in strained beauty, on a table at the east side of the room, where its clarity glistened in the sun's rays.

What would happen to the house? Would her father move now that he was no longer tied to Runford? Would he sell all the treasures he had gathered and she had learned to love?

Outside, the snow crunched under her booted feet and the crisp cool air bit her cheeks. She welcomed the cold. She could feel the cold. It was here and now and it forced her to pull the fur collar of her coat up higher around her chin, and it forced

16

away thoughts of summer and the hot sun on her damp skin.
. . .

She settled inside the car and put it in gear, her mind returning to the reason Ross Leyton was in Runford. Why hadn't her father said anything to her about selling the plant? Why hadn't he taken her into his confidence as he had so many times in the past? Why lock her out now when she had shared so many evenings of discussion on ways to increase their profits? Why had he purposely decided to shut her out and present it to her—all signed, sealed, and delivered?

Because he was afraid you would talk him out of it, the way you always have, her mind whispered. *And he didn't want to be talked out of it this time. He wanted to be free of the plant and its responsibilities. . . .*

A wisp of smoke curled out of the chimney of one of the old Victorian-style houses on Elm Street, drifted up to the top of a hill and dissipated into the clear blue sky. The town of Runford, New York, was nestled into the hollow next to the river, its houses sitting flat in the valley. Only a few clung to the hillside. It had seemed like a marvelous idea to those first settlers to build their dwellings next to the river, but in the spring, when the river swelled with melting snow and overflowed its banks, today's tenants wished the town's founders had had more foresight.

She drove past the glassworks, a low flat building sprawled on nearly two acres of land, gray and forbidding even in the bright sun, the smoke from the furnaces rising from the three chimneys. She forced her eyes away from the plant, her heart heavy. Even if Ross Leyton had assured Runford employees that they would continue as they had, the pride she felt at knowing her name was carried on some of the finest glass in the world would vanish. For her, nothing would be the same.

On Farragut Street she turned the car into the sloping driveway of an old house with gingerbread trim that had been painted a bright yellow.

The minute she opened the right side of the double oak door, music from a flute, a piano, and a violin assailed her ears. Karen, at the front desk, looked up and flashed a smile at her that was as bright as the morning. "Hello, Miss Runford. Great to see the sun, isn't it?"

"Yes, it is. Has Mr. Adams come in yet this morning?"

Karen shook her head. "Should I tell him you want to see him when he does?"

"Yes, please."

She walked past the desk and the two living rooms that served as a makeshift recital hall, and rounded the corner to open the door of her office. Tucked away under the stairs, there was relative peace and quiet here. She had installed the accoustical tiles on the asymetrical ceiling and the bright yellow carpeting on the walls herself. She had barely taken her coat off and tucked her purse away in the bottom drawer of the desk when the door, which she had left partially open, was pushed back.

She looked up and smiled, expecting to see Michael standing in the doorway. But it was Jane who stood there gazing at her, Jane in her usual outfit of khaki shirt and jeans, a maroon sweater thrown over her shoulders, her hair scraped back from her face and caught with an elastic band. "Is it true about your father selling the glassworks?"

Her thin face strained toward Anne as if her life depended on Anne's answer. Anne sat down in the swivel chair behind the desk and gazed at her. Jane had her violin under her arm; she had obviously just come from a lesson. "Yes, it's true."

"Does Michael know?"

"I'm not sure I understand what business that is of yours."

The girl had the grace to color and look away. "This school means a lot to him." Her eyes moved back to Anne. "It's his whole life."

"I'm aware of that."

"He needs the funds that you provide every year—"

An iciness touched her nerves. "I wasn't aware that Michael discussed his finances with you."

18

The look Jane fastened on her was contemptuous "There's a lot you aren't aware of." She ran from the room, and Anne could hear the soft thump of her feet on the treads of the stairs over her head, even through the soundproofing.

She leaned forward and clasped her shaking hands on the desk. A flash from the ring on her left hand played around the odd-shaped room. Why had Michael confided in Jane? It was an unpleasant question that had all kinds of ramifications. In the six months before she had been engaged to him, she had never seen him with Jane socially. They did spend a great deal of time together, rehearsing and playing in the faculty string quartet, but once when Anne had mentioned her admiration for Jane's talent, he had responded in a condescending tone, "Yes, I suppose she's good."

At her elbow, the phone rang. It was Michael. "Darling, the blasted car won't start. Could you possibly come and get me? I have to give a lesson at ten."

"Yes, of course."

She gathered up her coat and purse and walked back out to the lobby. Karen raised an eyebrow.

She said, "I'm going to pick up Michael. If there are any calls for me, I'll be back in a few minutes."

Karen shook her head. "Tell him he'd better trade off that heap."

When Anne picked Michael up in front of his house, he said almost the same thing. "I've got to trade the stupid thing off," he grumbled, climbing into her little car and folding his long legs under the dash. "It's driving me crazy."

"It's not driving you anywhere, that's the problem." A smile lifted her lips.

He ran a slim hand through his wheat-colored hair. "Don't be so bloody precise, not this morning, darling. I don't think I can take it."

It wasn't the first time Michael had failed to respond to her

19

wry, playful sense of humor. But this morning, under the pressure of events, she shot back, "It was a joke, nothing more."

He sent her a startled look. "I'm sorry. I'm taking my frustration about the car out on you, aren't I?"

"Everybody has car trouble at one time or another," she said.

"Yes," he responded, "but I have trouble all the time—because I'm too damn poor to fix up the one I've got, or buy another that's dependable."

"You know I'd be glad to stop by and pick you up—"

His no was short and clipped. "I'll get up early enough to jog to the school tomorrow. I need the exercise to improve my playing stamina."

She glanced at him. As usual he was neatly dressed, in dark pants, a white turtleneck sweater under a heavy tweed suit coat, and natural leather gloves. No overcoat, ever, even in the coldest weather. She knew, though she had never stayed the night with him, that he slept with the window open all winter and kept his room at a chilly fifty degrees.

She turned the car into the driveway of the yellow house and pulled into the parking space she had just left. As he was climbing out of the car she asked casually, "Have you seen the morning papers yet?"

He made an exasperated sound. "No. I went out to try to start the car the first thing this morning. I kept trying till I ran the battery down. Then I called you. Is it something important?"

"Well, yes, I—do you have a minute?"

When they walked into the school, Michael was frowning. "Karen, if my student comes, will you tell him I'll be up in a minute?"

"He's already here, Mr. Adams. He said he knew he was early."

Michael shook his head and caught Anne's elbow. "We'll have to make it quick, darling. He's from out of town, and his father doesn't like to wait for him."

20

He guided her into her office and shut the door. A slim hand went to his suit jacket and he pulled it open. "What's up?"

She took off her coat and hung it on the old-fashioned spindle hat rack she had installed in one corner. "I just found out this morning that—Dad is selling the glassworks."

The ruddy color in his cheeks seemed to drain away. "You just found out? What do you mean you just found out?"

She stood on the other side of the desk, making its broad wooden top a barrier between them. "I mean I read it in the paper this morning—and that was the first I had heard about it."

Slim fingers went up to thread through already tortured hair. Then he turned abruptly to stare out of the one narrow window. His voice was strained when he spoke. "Does this mean you'll be withdrawing your financial support of the school?"

"I—don't know. I don't know what my father's financial picture will be—now."

Michael's voice took on a bitter cast. "But his contributions will no longer have a tax advantage."

"I—suppose that's true."

He whirled around. "You suppose! He's your father, for God's sake! Don't you know?"

"He hasn't seen fit to confide in me about any of this."

His eyes glittered. "I should think you'd make it your business."

"How could I know?" she cried. "I had no idea he was even thinking about selling."

"Don't you talk to each other?" He leaned over the desk and placed his palms on it, confronting her. "Didn't you ever ask him how things were going?"

"I didn't have to," she said stiffly. "I knew he wasn't making money."

"You knew he wasn't making money." The flat words sounded hollow against the carpeted walls. "Why didn't you tell me?"

She looked at him then, her eyes sparkling with hurt anger. "I really didn't see what business it was of yours."

"You didn't see—" He bit off the words and made an exaggerated gesture with his hand. "Look, I've got to go. We'll have to continue this discussion later. Let's have lunch together at the Atrium, shall we?" He stepped around the desk and took her in his arms to brush his lips over her forehead. He held her for a moment longer. She stood unmoving in his arms—and unmoved. He held her away and said, "This doesn't change a thing between us, you know that. I still love you."

He gave her another quick kiss and strode out the door. She stared after him for a moment and then sat down at the desk, feeling an aching emptiness inside.

Her hand found the cool dome of her glass paperweight. Absently she rubbed her fingers over the glass and gazed at the bit of thistledown caught forever in flight inside.

The paperweight had become her talisman—just as Michael had. She had used him to touch, to hold, to call her own and keep away the disturbing thoughts that always threatened to come rushing in.

He had come into her life at a time when she had almost resigned herself to the fact that she was incapable of loving anyone.

She gripped the glass paperweight tighter. She did love Michael—she knew she did. She gazed at the thistledown trapped inside the glass, remembering. She had been at the school for nearly three years when the woman who had been director for many years retired. Then the board had hired Michael Adams, a young graduate student, to replace her. Anne hadn't even liked him, not at first. But Michael had pursued her almost from the moment he arrived at the school. She had put him off until one night he had caught her here in her office, cast aside his normal platonic manner, and kissed her senseless. He had been warm and real and wonderful, and she had known then that she wanted to stop running. His arms became a haven from the relentless grind of her memories. But she had to warn him—tell him the truth. "I want you to know—I— There was someone else—once."

He had stared at her with incredulous amazement. "My darling. I'd be astonished if there hadn't been. You surely don't think I expect you to be untouched at your age."

He had laughed and kissed her, and his tenderness had wiped away the anguished hours of remembering and given her such blessed relief, she had loved him then as never before.

Now her haven was gone.

She shook away her disturbing thoughts and walked across the hall to her studio. From her chair beside the piano bench, she said things automatically. "Hello, Scott. How are you today? Did you have a good week? Problems with the Bach? Well, let's see what we can do."

It was a relief to clear her mind and concentrate on the music. She taught four lessons that morning, and when the last long-legged girl hurried away, she rose from the chair, feeling suddenly stiff, as if her muscles had been straining to perform some task she was unused to.

She crossed the hall to her office, snatched up her purse and coat, and went back out to Karen.

"Oh, Miss Runford. Mr. Adams wants me to tell you he's been delayed. He wants you to go on ahead. He said he'd meet you there."

"Doesn't he want me to wait for him?"

Karen shook her head. "No. He insisted that you go on and order your lunch."

She stepped into the brilliant sunshine. The biting cold nipped her face and the snow crunched under her feet. She followed the small trail Karen had shoveled on the sidewalk and got into her car, glad to get out of the wind at least. The surrounding hills protected the town from the east and west, but in the winter, chill breezes blew along the river valley from the north.

Now a chilly breeze had blown in, and she shuddered and put the car in gear.

She wished she hadn't agreed to have lunch with Michael. She should have spent the hour talking to her father.

But to what purpose? Everything had been done, without her knowledge or consent . . . not that it was needed.

That was a rationalization—and she knew it. She knew why she hadn't lifted the phone at once and demanded to see her father. She couldn't run the risk of confronting . . . *him*.

Why, of all the companies in the world, had her father chosen to sell to Western Data Systems? Had Carson Leyton's guilty conscience goaded him into offering a far higher fee for the Runford Glassworks than anyone else? She thrust the thought away and pulled into the parking lot of the Atrium.

There were the usual small businesses in Runford: an insurance office, an appliance store, a grocery store, a feed and farm supply, and even a newly opened computer store. The men and women who worked in these offices and stores were the clientele of the Atrium, which was a Victorian house that had been converted by an Italian couple. They had raised the ceiling and added a glass skylight, making the interior an eye-pleasing mixture of cedar and windowpanes. Anne walked inside, conscious as always of light and space and green plants. She was shown to a table where she had a clear view of the street. She took off her coat and was barely settled into the comfortable plush chair when a green Volkswagen drove up outside the café and Michael got out. He didn't immediately walk up the steps to come inside. Instead, he leaned over the open door on the passenger side to talk to the driver of the car. She caught a glimpse of his profile, ruddy with the cold—or anger, perhaps?

He concluded his conversation with a quick slam of the car door. When he was inside, striding across the room to her, she knew she had guessed correctly. Michael, the most even-tempered of people, was blazingly angry.

The minute his eyes met hers, he forced a smile to his face. When he reached her table, he leaned over and kissed her lightly on the lips. "Darling, I am sorry."

"I'm just glad you got a ride so quickly. Was that Jane's car?"

The dark look returned. "Yes." He took up the menu with a forced air of congeniality. "What looks good today?"

"I haven't really thought about it. The braised chicken, perhaps. That's always good."

Michael stared at the menu with the same minute concentration he gave a cello score. Tall and slim as he was, he had a voracious appetite. He settled finally on a steak, baked potato, and salad, while Anne ordered a julienne salad.

"No pasta?" He smiled at her and covered her hand on the table with his long, slim-fingered one. "Angelina will be crushed."

She returned his smile. "Do you know what all that lovely pasta does to a girl's figure?"

His eyes moved over her. "I wouldn't think you'd have to worry."

The waitress came over, and both of them refused the offer of a drink. "I'd like the herbal tea if you have it," Michael told the girl, and she nodded and went away.

Over the table, Michael's eyes met Anne's. "Tell me about this merger."

She dropped her gaze to the bright orange cloth on the table and toyed with her knife, wanting very much to remove her hand from Michael's grasp. "I don't know any more about it at this point than anyone else. It's in the papers this morning. I knew Dad had considered selling a few years ago, but I thought he had changed his mind."

"Well, go on."

She shook her head, and his fingers tightened. He said, "Why do I have this distinct feeling you're keeping something from me—for all the wrong reasons?"

She was saved from answering by the presence of the waitress, who brought Michael's tea, but then the woman left them alone again.

"Are you keeping something from me?" he persisted.

"I'm sorry. I can't talk about it."

His mouth tightened but he didn't argue. "All right. Let's talk about the new owner of the glassworks. Could he be persuaded to continue the same beneficiary aid your father instituted?"

She stared at him. "You can't be serious."

"I assure you I am." She sensed there was an impatience in him that he was fighting to control. "The school can't exist without the support we've come to expect from your father."

"But surely if we raised the price of lessons and did some fund raising . . ."

His mouth twisted. "Be sensible, Anne. You know there's no way we could raise fifteen thousand dollars a year in Runford. Now, look, the head executive of Western is still here in town, talking to your father, isn't he?"

Her gaze dropped to the table. "I don't know."

"Well, find out. See him. Talk to him. Tell him our situation here. Surely when one company buys out another, it picks up the obligations as well as the assets."

"But this isn't a true obligation. This is just something my father did to help the people of this town have an access to the arts that they couldn't have afforded themselves."

"And you don't want to go begging to a stranger, do you? Well, never mind. I shouldn't have asked. I'm the head of the school. It's my job. I'll go see him."

A hard knot of fear clamped around her stomach. "No!" He shot her a sharp look, and she forced herself to calmness. "No. I don't think you should—until—until I've talked to my father. Perhaps—perhaps he's made some arrangements . . . for the school."

He brightened at once. "Yes, that's entirely possible, isn't it?"

Their food arrived, and Michael watched with anticipation as the savory steak was set before him. He was immediately absorbed with his food, picking up his knife and fork, cutting and tasting. "Well, perhaps you're right," he said, his eyes half closing in sensory enjoyment. "It wouldn't do to go off half-cocked to this new man and set him against us in the very beginning, would it?"

He didn't even notice the dryness in her tone. "No, it wouldn't." Her food seemed like ashes in her mouth.

He ate in silence for several moments and then said, "Are you free this afternoon?"

"Why?"

"I think the sooner we get this whole thing cleared up, the better. Cancel your lessons and go see your father. That way you can tell me anything you've found out at dinner tonight—discreetly, of course."

She made a wry grimace. "Should I wear my trench coat and report to you in code?"

He was distracted from his eating long enough to look up and raise an eyebrow at her. "Have you ever thought that perhaps you occasionally . . . misdirect that sense of humor of yours?"

Her mind played back an almost forgotten memory of another man's dry voice. *"You like to hide behind one-liners, don't you?"*

"I'm sorry. It's been a difficult morning and I—"

He glanced up then, his eyes warm with sympathy. "I'm sorry, too. Here I am going on at you about the school when you're worried about your father. But surely this sale is a good thing for him—if he's in a financial bind."

"I hope you're right." But she couldn't help but think that while the sale of Runford Glassworks might be good for her father, anything that brought Ross Leyton back into her life had to be labeled as disastrous.

CHAPTER TWO

An hour later, in her office, Anne dialed the familiar number, her fingers cold. Her father's secretary put her through at once. When he said hello, she responded conventionally and then asked, "I need to—see you, Dad. Are you free this afternoon?"

"Since when have you needed an appointment to see me?" An uncharacteristic heartiness sent a shiver through her. His voice echoed in her ear—a sure sign that he had switched on the conference phone speaker and their conversation was audible to anyone in the room. She knew at once that her father wanted someone else to hear her end of the conversation, and that that someone was Ross Leyton.

"I know you're busy. I didn't want to disturb you." By some miracle her own voice sounded coolly polite.

"You've seen the papers, then." It was a cautious question, a testing of her emotional barometer.

Her answer was guarded. "Yes, I've seen them." Her voice continued to sound normal, the control she had learned years ago functioning automatically. "Are you—with anyone?"

There was a hesitation. Then he said, "Right at the moment, yes. I'll be finished in about"—she could almost see him pull his cuff back to look at the digital watch she had given him at Christmastime,—"half an hour. Want to come over then?"

"Half an hour is fine."

She put down the phone quickly, as if to break even that fragile connection with the room where Ross stood with her father.

She thought she had her nerves under control when she arrived at the plant. The burly, gray-haired security guard smiled at her. "Playing hooky from school, Miss Runford?"

"My boss gave me the afternoon off, Charlie." Her smile answered his.

He chuckled. "Would you talk to my boss and see if he'll let me have the afternoon off, too?"

When she nodded, he waved her through the open gate, and she thought ruefully that her days of exchanging banter with Charlie Harris would soon be at an end.

A tour guide was taking a group of people through the plant. About a dozen of them were clustered around a woman who was saying, "We know that the Egyptians made and used glass. Some of the finest examples from antiquity are shown in this drawing . . ."

The guide's voice faded away as Anne climbed the stairs and turned into the carpeted corridor that led to her father's office. She stood outside the door for a minute, gathering her nerve. *Don't do this,* she admonished herself, *it's been ten years. He's probably forgotten all about you.*

She had hoped against hope that her father would interpret her phone call correctly, that she had an urgent need to speak to him alone. At any rate it seemed highly unlikely that Ross Leyton would still be in his office when she got there.

She was wrong. It wasn't highly unlikely, it was a cold fact. He was there—and her father was not.

He had his back to her, looking out the window. His profile in silhouette was all she saw at first, but it was enough. A lean male clothed in a light-gray suit—a suit probably more appropriate to California's mild climate than New York's winters—he looked taller than even his six feet two inches, the proud lift of head more lethally male than ever. At the sound of the door opening, he turned slowly. Sensual memories roused and stirred, went shivering down her spine to the primitive core at its base.

"Hello, Anne."

Saliva climbed in her throat and clung. She hadn't said his name aloud in ten years. "Hello, Ross."

She wasn't going to back out of the room like a coward, but it went against every instinct she had to step inside and close the door. "Where is—my father?"

Eyes of a deep, dark gray gazed at her from under the black brows. "I could lie," he said softly, "and say he just stepped out, but I think you're intelligent enough to guess it's no accident I'm here." There was a hint of challenge in the bland tone.

Standing in the middle of the room as she was, she felt vulnerable. She walked to a high-backed leather chair that sat in front of the desk and clutched it with both hands, thankful that it hid the contours of her body from him.

As if to counter her move, he left his position by the window and moved to the desk, where he lifted a hip and seated himself on the corner.

Ten years ago, at the age of twenty-five, he had not been president of a large corporation, but there had always been that air of self-assured maleness about him. Now, with maturity, it had intensified. There was about Ross an air of controlled intensity, of a male animal able to protect what is his. The full head of black hair was touched with gray at the temples now, but the jaw and chin were more squarely set than ever. There was a slashing line that deepened on the side of his face when he smiled, which, on anyone else, might have been called a dimple.

"Take off your coat," he said in that same low tone.

"I really hadn't planned to stay," she replied. "You don't know when my father is returning?"

"He'll return when I signal his secretary that we're through talking."

30

It was a flat statement, brooking no protest. Her fingers bit into the leather. "I didn't realize you were going to—assume control of Runford today."

His mouth tightened. "I'm not assuming control of Runford, today or ever."

"Appearances to the contrary," she said sharply.

"Stop it." The low voice gave the order coolly. "I didn't initiate this meeting to indulge in a fencing match with you."

"No, I don't suppose you did. You've already won all the battles, haven't you? Perhaps we should rename Runford and call it Carthage."

He eased off the desk and took a step toward her. "I'll ask you once again to take off your coat and sit down. If you don't"—his eyes traveled over her face and rested on her mouth—"I think you might regret it."

She stood her ground and stared back at him, the light of battle in her eyes. Then a voice inside her whispered, *That's what you want, isn't it? You want him to take you in his arms and kiss you even if it is in anger. . . .*

The thought was intolerable and goaded her into action. She dropped her purse over the back of the chair and unbuttoned her coat and shrugged out of it, folding it over her arm and carrying it protectively in front of her as she walked around the chair and settled into it. Letting the coat lie like a bulky heap in her lap, she raised a cool face to him, unaware that her tawny eyes had gone dark with emotion. "What did you want to talk to me about?"

He shifted his position to the front of the desk. He was so close, she could have reached out and touched his trousered legs. Even while she stilled the muscles of her face and body, he let the silence in the room grow. Then he said, "How involved in this music school are you?"

It was not what she had expected. "Very. It's my living and my life."

He glanced down at her hand that lay on top of the folded

coat. "Your father says you are engaged to the director of the school, a Michael Adams, I believe."

Her temper flared. "What do you want . . . confirmation of my father's information?"

He stretched out his arms and wrapped his fingers around the edge of the desk. His knuckles went white with the strength of his grip. "I have, perhaps, worded my questions incorrectly. What I want to know is, could you manage to take a week off—soon?"

She lifted her chin. "For what purpose?"

"For the purpose of seeing your mother."

Her sharply indrawn breath sounded like a gun shot. "No."

He loosened his grip on the desk and leaned forward. "Anne, your mother wants to see you and your sister. The circumstances are such that she can't travel." His words were cool and reasonable.

"No," she said. "I'm sorry. I have too many commitments here."

He said a short, succinct word. "Commitments that are more important than making contact with a mother you haven't seen in ten years?"

Her eyes flashed. "She made the rules, I'm only following them. She didn't want either of her daughters ten years ago. Why should she feel any different now?"

"As I said, circumstances have changed."

"For her? They haven't changed for Shari and me. When your father wanted her, she left us without a second thought to go with him. We learned to live without her then. We'll continue to do so."

"And I believed you were a mature adult who would listen to reason." The words were toneless, but they cut with a fine precision.

His strategic position kept her a prisoner in her chair. To rise to her feet would bring her far too close to that hard mouth. "Was that all you wanted?"

32

With a lithe movement of his upper body, he leaned forward and grasped the arms of her chair, trapping her. "No. That's not all I wanted." He was so close, she could see the fine pores of his skin, the gray-black of his eyes with their blue flecks, the full curve of his mouth. Her nose was filled with the clean male scent of him.

Even though it cost her the earth, she met his gaze without flinching. "Stop trying to frighten me, Ross." Her voice trembled. Her control was almost gone.

"Is that what I'm doing?" He leaned forward still farther and the edge of his jacket brushed the top of her hand. While she was trying to recover from the shock of that slight contact, his mouth found her temple. "I thought I was trying to recapture something I lost a long time ago—"

"You can't—" His mouth covered hers, effectively stopping her words. His lips were warm and disturbing, discovering the contours of hers with a gentleness she remembered well. She lifted her hands to push him away, but it was like pushing a wall of rock and, instead, her hands found a sensual pleasure in touching the light wool jacket and the hard body underneath.

She couldn't move. Her head tipped back, she was his prisoner, held captive in the chair by his mouth and nothing else— except the stirring of her own long-buried yearnings. Every inch of her body seemed to leap to life and demand that she respond, that she open her mouth to his gently probing tongue. Her cheeks burned with the desire that flared in the pit of her stomach. She ached with need—a need that he alone had taught her.

She twisted her head and broke off the kiss. He moved back just enough to let his gaze encompass her entire face. His slight smile made her flare with anger—and self-contempt. "It must," she said, her voice low and trembling, "be something in the moon. Is it a ten-year cycle, Ross? Have you run through so many women, you're having to start at the bottom of the list all over again?"

He took her jibe with silent stoicism, his eyes pinning her to the place where she sat. "There is no list." The words were clipped, barely polite. "But if there was, you'd be at the top, not the bottom."

The husky intensity in his voice almost convinced her that he meant it. To fight the clamor inside her, the aching wish that it were true, she struck out wildly with her words. "That's quite a compliment coming from the supreme connoisseur of women."

His eyes narrowed. "Is that what you think I am?"

She tried to make her voice sound uncaring. "I read the papers occasionally to see what the West Coast jet set is doing. You're always included—you and your current lady."

He slanted her a dry look. "You were interested enough to keep track?"

Hotly she said, "I wasn't interested in you. I was only interested in seeing that your style hasn't changed, that's all."

The sardonic smile vanished. His eyes wintery, he said, "You're very quick to judge—and condemn—when you don't know all the facts." It was a cool statement that disturbed her more than a violent denial might have.

"I know everything about you I need to know."

The slight negative movement of his head was slow and purposeful. "You haven't even begun." The dark straight eyelashes dropped partially over his eyes. "I mean to rectify that. Have dinner with me tonight."

Astounded, she said, "You can't be serious."

"I don't give dinner invitations in jest." He paused and then added, "If it makes any difference, we won't be alone. My assistant will be dining with us."

She fought down the mental picture of sitting across the table from Ross, watching him, listening to him talk . . . "I'm sorry. My fiancé and I are going out this evening."

If he was disturbed by the refusal, not a muscle in his face betrayed him. "All right," he said easily. "Perhaps tomorrow night."

She shook her head. "I'm tied up tomorrow night." When he

lifted his lips in a slight, unbelieving smile, she explained, "There is a recital at the school. I couldn't possibly disappoint my students."

The smile became genuine. He folded his arms across his chest. "Yes, I can see where they might need moral support." He relaxed against the desk and favored her with an amused look. "I remember those days. My mouth was always dry and my hands were always wet." She was acutely uncomfortable under his gaze. It was as if he were forcing her to remember how they had played piano duets together. . . . His low voice cut into her thoughts. "Is this recital open to the public?"

With an effort, she returned to cool civility. "Yes, of course. Why? Will you—still be in town then?"

"Oh, yes," he said softly. "I'll be in town until I—complete my business."

"But I thought your business with my father was finished." There was an edge to her tone.

"It is. You're the one who constitutes my unfinished business." The words were gentle but there was steel in them.

"I won't change my mind about seeing Leora," she said flatly.

An eyebrow lifted. "Let's leave it for now, shall we?" He swiveled his upper body around and, without hesitation, punched the correct button beside the telephone to signal to the outside world that they were finished.

Incredulous that he should be prepared to devote his time to something her mother obviously wanted badly, she said, "You can't mean you're staying in Runford until you convince me to go."

He turned to give her a bland look. "That's exactly what I do mean."

Her face warmed with the heat of her anger. "Then I suggest you buy a house—*because you're going to be here for the rest of your life.*"

She thrust herself up out of the chair. At the slight brush of her body against his, every nerve she had trembled. She clamped down on her emotional reaction, but even as she walked to the door she was still sharply aware of the man who leaned against the front of the desk with his arms folded. She had escaped him, only because he allowed it.

The door swung open just as she reached for the knob. Her father stood in the doorway and his surprise at seeing her would have been comical if she had felt like laughing.

"Hello." His eyes flickered anxiously over her face and then skittered past her shoulder to Ross. "Everything all right?"

With a little shock, she realized that Owen Runford had known exactly why Ross had wanted to speak to her.

"We've agreed to disagree for the time being," Ross said easily from behind her.

"Then you told him no," her father said, and she was amazed to see the dismayed glance he gave Ross.

Thoughts as searing and disturbing as lightning flashes sizzled through her mind. "Father, you didn't by any chance make a trade, did you?"

Her father's face reddened. "You always were a quick child." He put his hands on her shoulders in a suppliant gesture.

She faced him, her eyes demanding that he tell her the truth. "And is this deal contingent on Shari and I visiting our mother?" She felt the corners of her mouth tremble as she waited for him to deny it, prayed that he would.

He hesitated, and from behind her, Ross's voice said shortly, "No. The merger is an accomplished fact."

The cool words did not give her the easiness of mind they should have. There was still something they weren't telling her.

Owen Runford's face pleaded for understanding. "I did promise them a chance to speak to you, honey, but that was all. It has to be your decision to go."

She twisted out of her father's arms, feeling utterly betrayed. "How could you possibly do this?" He only stared back at her with anguish in every line of his face and made a gesture with his hand toward her.

36

The urge to lash out made her turn to face her other adversary. "I don't believe this, any of it. Did your father actually buy an entire company for the sole purpose of pleading his wife's case to her daughters?"

Ross Leyton didn't move a muscle from his place in front of the desk. "My father has a motto," he said, in that low, totally male voice. " 'Take what you want—and pay for it.' "

"Yes," she returned heatedly. "That sounds like your father."

"Anne—" Her father reached out to her again, but she shook her head.

"I can't stay and discuss it. I'm due back at the school." She took a step forward and then turned. "I'll be in late tonight, don't wait up." She pressed her mouth to her father's cheek. He managed a weak smile.

"All right, honey. Take care. I'll talk to you tomorrow."

She drove back to the school. While she taught she kept her thoughts at bay. But when her lessons were over and she walked out to the car to go home, there was no longer any distraction to keep them from flooding in.

She drove through the snowy streets automatically, her thoughts running around like rabbits in her head. Her mother's affair, divorce, and subsequent marriage to Carson Leyton happened long ago. It was ancient history. It should have no power over Anne now. And yet, as Anne was on the very brink of marriage, her mother was intruding on her life once again.

She couldn't let that happen—the way it had when she was seventeen. She had just come home from school that day in October when her mother summoned her to her bedroom. "I have to go, darling. It's the only way. I can only pray for your understanding." There were tears in her mother's eyes, but Anne was caught in a fierce sense of disbelief. This couldn't be happening to her parents. Her mother had continued, "Promise me you'll take care of Shari."

She couldn't believe it, any of it. "But we'll be seeing you— won't we, Mother?" Her eyes had searched her mother's face, desperate for some sign of agreement. "We'll be going out to California to stay with you . . ." She loved her mother, needed her. How could she have lived, knowing she would never again see the woman who had borne her?

Her mother had shaken her head. "No, I'm afraid not, darling. There are . . . reasons that I can't explain right now. Carson travels extensively, and I want to be with him. I couldn't—be a good mother to you and Shari if I were constantly packing to go someplace, now, could I?" She had smiled at Anne, a determined, bright smile, though there were tears in her eyes.

And in that moment Anne had grown up. She realized with stunning clarity that she had idolized a woman who was going to walk away from her and never come back. She had stood stock-still in the room, clenched her fists, and made a solemn vow that she would never care about anyone enough to feel that devastated again. And that summer she had fallen in love with Ross . . . and been rejected. . . .

Now Ross wanted her to see her mother again. She couldn't do it. She couldn't forgive—or forget. She had loved them both, and they had pushed her away. There was Shari to think about, too. Anne would never allow the young girl to be exposed to her mother's will-o'-the-wispish affections.

It isn't Shari you're protecting, it's yourself. A few short hours ago, he had kissed her—and she had responded! She was wearing Michael's ring—and she had allowed, even returned, Ross's kiss. She couldn't let that happen again. At all costs she had to stay away from Ross Leyton. He was like a flame she had always been drawn to, strains of a melody she had never forgotten.

She would see him tomorrow and tell him *no* in no uncertain terms. A man who headed a conglomerate like Western couldn't afford to spend days on end in Runford. He would go away, and her life would resume its normal pattern of teaching and seeing Michael. She would marry him—and she would be safe. Shari and she would both be safe.

Sure that she had made the right decision, she climbed the

stairs to her room and shed her jacket, tossing it casually on the bed. She opened the closet door and gazed inside, trying to think what to wear for her evening out. She was still there when Shari stuck her head around the door. "Hi, are you decent?"

Anne made a face at her. "Of course. Come in."

The younger girl sauntered to the bed and sat down with a thump on the edge. "Where are you going tonight?"

"I'm not sure." Her lips curved in a half-smile. "Michael's complaining about money again, so I thought I might take him to the Inn tonight."

"Lucky Michael." Shari leaned back, supporting herself on her palms against the spread. "Do you really like him, Anne?"

"Of course. Now be quiet a minute so I can think what to wear."

"But how can you? I mean he's so—weird."

The dark-green velvet blazer, she thought, with her tweed skirt and the cream-colored silk blouse with the tie at the neck. Hooking her fingers around the hangers, she brought her choices out of the closet. "What do you mean—weird?"

Shari lifted one slim shoulder. "I don't know, he just is. He isn't the kind of guy I picture you with at all." She kicked off her shoes and tucked her nylon-stockinged feet up under her to sit cross-legged.

Anne shook her head as she laid her clothes on the bed and crossed to her dresser.

"I mean, look at you," Shari persisted. "Gorgeous hair, sexy eyes . . . and it's all wasted on him. You don't belong with somebody like Michael. All he thinks about is his stupid cello."

Anne picked up her eyeliner and drew a thin dark line around her underlid. "Haven't we had this conversation before?"

"I learned about assertiveness training in school today. If you want to convince people of something, you have to keep saying it over and over—like a broken record."

"What ever happened to math and English?" Her voice was dryly tolerant.

"We still have them." Shari was not to be sidetracked. "We read part of *Julius Caesar* in English today. That's why I got to thinking about Michael. He reminds me of him."

"Michael reminds you of Julius Caesar?" She applied the dusky gray eyeshadow with quick, deft strokes of the feathery brush.

"No, not Julius Caesar, silly, his assassin, Cassius. The one with the lean and hungry look. Michael Adams always looks as if he's hungry."

Anne was unperturbed. "He does have a rather good appetite."

"Is he a good lover—or don't you know?"

The brush stopped. She raised her eyes to meet Shari's in the mirror. "That's really none of your business." Her dry tone didn't deter her sister.

"I suppose you can't tell whether a man's a good lover just by looking at him, can you?" She tilted her head, considering the thought.

"Not usually," Anne agreed dryly, glad that Shari had switched from her specific case to more general ones.

"Why is it some men just look sexy?" Shari frowned in concentration. "Like Jeff Overholzer. I'd be in seventh heaven if he ever noticed me." Shari expelled a short breath, and Anne hid a smile, thinking the lanky boy who was the basketball star at Runford could hardly be described as sexy. "And that Ross Leyton in today's paper. Boy, does he look like a super lover. Just think, if Mother had taken us with her when she married Carson Leyton, Ross would have been our step-brother. Wow!"

The hand that was applying lip gloss trembled. She took a tissue and wiped off the blurred color, forcing herself to calmness. "Well, she didn't, and he isn't."

Shari stared at Anne in the mirror. "But he is, isn't he—I mean, really. Just because we don't live with him . . ."

"Whatever relationship we may or may not have to Ross

Leyton doesn't make a bit of difference in our lives, honey. We don't belong in his world—and he doesn't belong in ours."

She undressed quickly, put on the silk blouse, and slid the wool skirt over her head, buttoning it around her slim waist. The long tie was wrapped around her neck ascot fashion and tied in a soft bow at her throat. She was pulling on the jacket when Shari said, "You look like you're going to New York for a business convention. How come you don't have any sexy clothes—you know, something daring and low-cut and slinky? You're not going to turn Michael on looking like that."

She tugged at her blouse to bring the cuffs out from under the velvet sleeves. "When I want you to orchestrate my love life, I'll let you know, okay?"

"Somebody ought to do it for you. Right now all it is is a sickening cello solo." She began to hum a syrupy version of Saint-Saëns's "The Swan," with an elaborate vibrato that imitated the sound of Michael's cello with uncanny accuracy.

Anne turned from the mirror and took two slow, menacing steps toward the girl. The humming increased in volume, became more soulful, and now was accompanied with the drawing of the bow back and forth over the imaginery stringed instrument between Shari's crossed legs.

Mock-menacing, she picked up a pillow. "Too bad they didn't teach you the difference between asserting yourself and being obnoxious." The pillow homed to its target, hitting Shari squarely in the face. The humming dissolved into a screech, and the girl toppled over backward, clutching the pillow and laughing.

Shari sat up, the pillow tucked beneath her arms in front of her.

Anne picked up her purse and coat. "Do us both a favor, will you? Turn that imagination and energy you've been focusing on my love life toward your homework."

"I only have one assignment to do—math. I have to call Heather to ask her about one of the problems."

"Well, don't stay on the phone for hours. Get to bed at a

decent time. You're planning on coming to the recital tomorrow night, aren't you?"

"I don't know." Shari shot her a wicked look. "Can I bring my cello and play my solo?"

Anne rolled her eyes heavenward. "Where have I failed?" She turned to walk out of the room—and stepped aside just in time to get nothing more than a glancing blow from the flying pillow that Shari had tossed in retaliation.

CHAPTER THREE

Michael bounded down the steps of the porch and slid into Anne's car beside her. He seemed in high spirits and kept the casual conversation going throughout the twenty-minute drive to the Inn. She was thankful for that, even though Shari's teasing had lightened her mood and helped her put her confrontation with Ross out of her mind. But once they were inside the luxurious Inn, and she was seated by the window before a view that took in miles of countryside, she lapsed into pensive thought. The snow-covered hills and valleys shone blue-white under an early moon, and bare-branched trees splayed dark shadows like fingers over the slopes. The flickering candle in the red bowl on the table was a warm and intimate contrast, but her frame of mind matched the scene beyond the window. Long shadows of memories darted through her mind, chilling her.

Throughout dinner Michael continued to talk until they had finished eating. But after the steward poured a second glass of wine and went away, Michael said, "You're very quiet. Have you had a hard day?"

"You might say that." She brushed back a straying strand of tawny hair.

He covered her hand with his. "I didn't want to spoil our dinner with business talk. But—have you spoken to your father?"

Guilty conscience seized her. She had been so shaken by her encounter with Ross, she had completely forgotten about the school's dilemma. "No. I—he was with—with someone when I—when I went to see him."

"You mustn't let this thing drag on, darling. We've got to know where we stand."

"I realize that." She tried not to sound defensive. "It's just that I—something else came up that I had to—handle."

His fingers tightened over hers. "You've looked rather distracted all evening. What is it?" She shook her head, but he refused to be put off. "Anne, don't shut me out. We're going to be married soon. Don't you think it's time you started confiding in me?"

He was right, she supposed. They were going to be married. He had a right to know something about her tangled family. She was silent for a moment and then said, "I'm sure it's not any secret to you that my mother left my father several years ago to marry another man."

Michael's eyes flickered away for a moment and then returned to her. "I had heard something about it, yes."

"That man was Carson Leyton."

From the expression on Michael's face, she could see that that was no surprise to him, either. "Go on."

"At the time, mother made the decision to step out of our lives—that is, Shari's and mine—entirely. We have not seen or heard from her for ten years." She took a breath. "Now it seems she wants to see us. Ro—Mr. Leyton—has asked us to agree to go to see her."

Michael's eyes lit up with delight. "Darling, that's marvelous."

She shook her head. "I told him no, of course. I—"

He drew back, astonished. "You didn't."

44

It was her turn to be amazed. "Of course I did." She stared at him, willing him to understand. "You can't think I want to see her now after all these years."

"But you must, don't you see?" He leaned forward and tightened his clasp on her hand. "If you can renew your friendship with your mother, Carson Leyton is certain to feel obligated to continue his support of the school."

"And that's more important to you than my feelings?" It was a plea for understanding, but it fell on deaf ears.

He brushed her words aside. "Right now, yes. Anne, for heaven's sake. The school has over two hundred students, and we're growing every week. Think about all the children who are getting a chance to study with excellent teachers, children who wouldn't know a fingerboard from a bow if we weren't here. You can't let your pride get in the way of the lives of so many people."

His eyes, burning with his zeal, locked with hers. Her voice a low husk, she said, "There's no guarantee that the Leytons will continue to fund the school even if I do—agree to see Leora."

Michael smiled a slow, charming smile. "Then make it a condition, darling."

Her nerves jumped and quivered. "You don't mean that."

He made an impatient movement with his free hand. "Of course I do. The Leytons want something—you want something. You make a deal. You go see your mother and exchange a few polite pleasantries, in return for which, Carson Leyton secures the future of the school. What could be simpler?"

"It isn't simple, believe me. Please, Michael, try to see it from my viewpoint. What can anyone possibly gain from resurrecting family relationships that don't exist anymore?"

"You're being obstructive. Family relationships exist whether they are recognized or not. She's still your mother, even if she hasn't been with you—"

"She isn't. . . ."

"Whether she is or isn't doesn't matter. The school is what matters. And right now, the school is in your hands." He took his hand from the top of hers and inserted it underneath to lift her fingers to his lips. "Your lovely, talented hands." The moistness of his mouth on her palm was unpleasant, and she had to fight not to snatch her hand away.

He lifted his head. "Tell Leyton that—" His gaze was fastened to a point over her shoulder. "Well, well, well. Speak of the devil. I believe your charming step-brother has just come into the Inn. No, don't turn. He's being seated with a woman two tables away."

"How—" Speaking was suddenly difficult. "How did you know him?"

"I recognized him from his picture in the paper." Michael went on openly staring. "The woman he's with is a knockout." Male appreciation gleamed in his eyes. With sudden, startling clarity, she realized that Michael had never once looked at her that way.

"She must be quite something."

Her dry words made his eyes flicker back to her. His hand covered hers again, his long fingers cool on her upper wrist. "You've never been jealous before." Amusement touched his lips. "I'm flattered."

She did withdraw her hand then, covering her defensive action by picking up her wineglass and sipping the dry white wine.

He asked, "Is Dina playing in the recital tomorrow night?"

She welcomed the change of topic. Her wineglass was returned to the table and, in the candlelight, the tension in her face smoothed away as she smiled slightly, thinking of her talented pupil. "Yes. She's playing Chopin's Waltz in C sharp minor."

Michael shook his head. "You know you have a prodigy on your hands, don't you?"

"I've told her parents she should be studying at Eastman or Julliard many times. They only shake their heads and say they can't afford the travel and the higher-priced lessons."

"She's doing well with you. I'm sure she could stay with you for another year or two and suffer no harm."

"Thank you." The bite of sarcasm crept into her voice, even though she tried to keep it out.

"Darling, don't be prickly. I know how proud you are of her and rightly so. You have a beautiful rapport with her." He reached out to his wineglass and twisted it on the red cloth, his eyes reflective. "If the school should close, we'd be forced to look for other jobs, you and I. You can't imagine we'd stay in Runford, can you?"

He lifted his wineglass and drank, his eyes watching her over the crystal rim. He had not changed the topic of conversation at all. He was subtly reminding her that her talented pupil would suffer if the school was forced to close. When he set the glass down, she said crisply, "Are you saying that Dina's future depends on my agreeing to Leyton's demands?"

"I'm saying that Dina's musical training depends on your staying in Runford. And you can only do that if the school remains operative. Otherwise, both you and I will be forced to go somewhere else, some larger city, to earn our living."

Her hand trembled on the table and she thrust it into her lap to be clenched inside her other one. "There is one other thing I think you should know," she said, forcing the words from the depth of her soul.

Michael's faint amused smile stayed firmly in place. "You sound positively ominous. What is it that's making you look like a thundercloud?"

"There is another reason I can't—do what you're asking." Her heart beat against her ribs with a slow, painful thud. She knew that in order to protect herself, she was going to have to tell Michael the truth, the truth she had never told any other living person.

"What is it?" He was placid, waiting, sure that whatever she had to say couldn't be that earthshaking.

"Once, a long time ago"—her voice was husky, as if her throat were closing protectively to keep the words inside, where they belonged—"I was—involved with Ross Leyton."

47

Michael sat for a moment, his eyes never leaving hers. Then his mouth relaxed into a drawn out *ah* and he murmured, "So that's it." He gave her a shrewd, assessing look. "I should have guessed."

Her eyes flashed. "What do you mean by that?"

He was immediately placatory. "I just meant I should have guessed there was another reason you were so adamant about not seeing your mother. Darling," he said persuasively, "what are you afraid of? You're a big girl now—and you belong to me. Whatever happened happened a long time ago. You're wearing my ring on your finger and you're going to marry me." He paused and gave her another shrewd glance. "I'm sure seeing him again has been difficult for you and perhaps caused your heart to give a few girlish flutters, but that's normal. He was your first love, I suppose."

She was silent, and he accepted her silence as affirmation.

"Well, then, there you are. There's nothing more to it than that." He folded the red cloth napkin and laid it beside his plate. "Darling, believe me, you're worrying about nothing. I'm sure he's forgotten you long ago, particularly in view of the delectable creature he's with tonight. So why don't we go to his table right now, and you can introduce me and then say that you've changed your mind and you would like to see your mother—if certain details can be worked out. Then ask to see him tomorrow. You can spring our little counter offer on him then."

"You make it sound so simple." Her tone was slightly acid.

His mouth tightened for a moment. Then he said easily, "It is simple. You're the one who's making it difficult." He sat back in his chair, his eyes narrowing with a speculative gleam. "Unless . . . you're still in love with him."

"Of course I'm not," she said quickly. The words seemed to reverberate in her ears.

He seemed not to notice the anxiety in her voice. "Well, then"—he gripped the edge of the table with his hands and levered his slim body upright—"let's get it done, shall we?"

Her face cool, her mind in a turmoil, she got to her feet.

He said, "Darling, don't forget the bill."

With an easy grace she leaned forward and picked it up, thinking as she did that he had no self-consciousness about allowing her to assume the male prerogative of paying. But then, Michael was pragmatic. He had told her frankly that if the evening was to be his treat, they would warm up spaghetti over his two-burner stove and spend the evening in his apartment, listening to John Cage's music. While she wouldn't have minded the spaghetti, she didn't share Michael's enthusiasm for the avant-garde composer. She was hopelessly addicted to the romantics—Tchaikovsky, Brahms, Rachmaninoff. Michael often teased her about her penchant for the past. "Come join the rest of us in the twentieth century," he'd say, and laugh and shake his head.

Now Michael held her coat for her and she turned to lift one arm and put it into the sleeve, when she saw Ross. The candle flame highlighted the planes of his cheeks and shadowed the deep-set dark eyes. He was smiling at something his companion had said, and his full, sensual mouth curved attractively at the corners.

Something curled in her stomach, an old, never-forgotten ache. Then, as if he sensed her gaze, he raised his eyes and captured hers for what seemed like a long moment. There was no surprise in his expression. He must have seen her when he entered the restaurant at the same time Michael spotted him.

Even though her heart was pounding, she managed to get her other arm into her coat. She would have turned away, but Michael made a sound and gave her a little push. Lifting her lips in a compulsory smile, she forced herself to walk the two steps to Ross's table. "Hello, Ross."

His gaze flickered over her shoulder to the man behind her. His smile changed, became cool even as he rose politely. "Hello, Anne."

The sight of him on his feet, as male and attractive as he had been in the office that afternoon, unnerved her further. He had changed to a dark-gray suit, one that fit him to perfection. Quickly, before she lost her courage, she said, "I'd like you to meet my fiancé, Michael Adams. Michael, this is Ross Leyton."

Michael stuck out his hand and said with overly bright enthusiasm, "Mr. Leyton. A pleasure to meet you, sir. Congratulations on acquiring Runford Glass."

Ross's dark head bowed briefly. "May I introduce my assistant, Nancy Hutchinson."

The woman turned her head and smiled at Michael. Beaming with pleasure, he stepped forward to take the hand that she offered.

She knew from the sound of her fiancé's voice he was saying something complimentary and effusive, but the words seemed to blur together like music that had no form, was meaningless sound. For Ross's eyes were on her, lazily following the narrow opening of her coat down to her waist.

Then Michael's voice stopped, and Ross said easily, "Sit down and have a drink with us."

"No, really, we were just on our way out—"

"But it's early," Michael interjected quickly, "and we could stay long enough to have one drink."

In three long strides he stepped around to the opposite side of the table and sat down next to Nancy Hutchinson, leaving Anne no alternative but to watch helplessly as Ross pulled back the chair next to his. Her ultrasensitive nerves felt the brush of his hand on the top of her shoulder through her coat as she sat down. Somewhere in the background soft music played, and she recognized the melody. It was a song that had been popular the year she was seventeen.

"May I help you with your coat?" She steeled herself to the reaction of her body to Ross's low, attractive voice over the background of music and turned to him. Her smile was artificial. "Yes, of course."

She made a shrugging motion to help the process along, but

the velvet sleeve of her blazer caught, and before she could protest, Ross's long fingers crept inside to hold the outer sleeve away from the inner one, the backs of his fingers brushing the sensitive pulse point on her wrist. Shivers of pleasure ascended her arm. Grimly she reminded herself that Ross's touch could mean nothing to her. Her head knew that. It was her body that wouldn't accept the fact.

Needing his reality, she looked at Michael. He was engrossed in talking to Nancy Hutchinson. She could see why. The woman was an attractive brunette, perhaps Anne's age or a little older. The simple white gown she wore was held in place by two narrow straps over her shoulders, shoulders that glowed with a golden California tan. Her dark hair was loose and flowing around her face.

She wondered if this attractive woman was Ross's current love. They had an air of belonging—two attractive, successful people who knew where they were going.

A movement next to her made her raise her eyes. Ross was watching her, something hard and alien glittering in his eyes. She shifted in her chair, wanting very much to escape that gaze, when he lifted his hand to signal the waiter. The fine lining of his jacket slipped against the silk of his shirt and the resulting sensuous sound made her nerves quiver with a newer, fiercer energy. She was thankful that the young man appeared at his elbow almost immediately.

"We'd like two more glasses, please," he said with the cool dismissal of one accustomed to giving orders.

The waiter nodded and went away. In a matter of seconds he was back with the glasses on a round tray.

She watched the wine being poured out, knowing she had already had her measure of alcohol for the evening. But even a crystal wineglass was something to hide behind. She lifted the drink to her lips.

The liquid went down her throat, cool and biting with the fruity taste of grapes. Whatever this was, it was an expensive

51

vintage for the connoisseur. She let her fingers linger on the stem of the wineglass, knowing she needed something to cling to in the evocative presence of Ross Leyton. Instinctively her fingers traced around the circular foot of the glass and lingered over a small imperfection.

"Not exactly Runford crystal, is it?" The murmured words did not interrupt Michael's conversation with Ross's assistant. They were talking about California and the beaches and surfing.

"What do you know about Runford crystal?"

Dark lashes fell over his eyes as he stared at her hand. "I know that glass is made from potash and sand, two opaque minerals that become transparent in high heat. I know that the clarity of the crystal depends on the purity of the raw material used. And the amount of lead. And I also know that it is the lead content that gives Runford crystal that bell-like tone when flicked with a fingernail, a tone that is characteristic of good crystal everywhere."

"You have been doing your homework, haven't you?"

He smiled slightly. "I never go into any venture without doing the research."

She hesitated for a moment. Then, driven by wine-strengthened courage, she said, "May I ask you something?"

His mouth quirked. "You can ask me anything—but I reserve the right to answer until after I've heard the question."

"Did my father contact yours—or was it the other way around?"

He sat for a moment, considering, and she had decided he wasn't going to answer her, when he said, "We sent a representative to your father when we heard he was looking for a buyer." There was another long pause and then he said softly, "Our representative had instructions to offer him double the amount any other party offered."

"How could you?" The words were low and intense, a barely concealed cry of pain.

He angled a brow upward. "That's the way the free enterprise system works. The one who has the money to buy—buys."

"And you bought me as well." Her voice was expressionless.

He reached for her wrist. "I thought your father made it clear to you that you were not included in the deal."

She said bitterly, "You must have known I'd feel some obligation."

"I was hoping you would, but I knew there was no guarantee."

Suddenly she realized that Michael had broken off his conversation and that both he and Nancy Hutchinson were staring at Ross's hand lying over hers on the table. She snatched her hand away and thrust it in her lap to be joined by her other one.

"You two seem to be making up for lost time in renewing your—family relationship," Michael said easily. "Have you told him about changing your mind about visiting your mother, darling?"

Ross's gaze sliced over her. "Have you changed your mind?"

"I'm not sure—"

Michael cut in smoothly, "If you're still going to be in town tomorrow night, you might like to attend the recital at the school. We have some very talented pupils performing. One of Anne's in particular we think has the makings of a concert pianist."

She stared at Michael, unable to believe he was using such blatant emotional blackmail. He was reminding her of Dina, forcing her to remember their earlier conversation. The music in the background changed, became modern and raucous.

She gathered herself and directed her words to Ross. "I need to talk to you about certain—details. I have an hour free between ten and eleven tomorrow. Perhaps you'd come by the office . . ."

He shook his head slowly, regretfully. "I'm sorry. That's impossible."

Michael's face mirrored his displeasure and Ross favored him with a slow, measured gaze. Then the older man said, "If you wouldn't mind cutting your evening short, I might stop by the house after I take Nancy home."

"No, I'd rather not—" she protested, but Michael interrupted.

"You know I never like to stay out late on a night before I play." Then, to Ross, "Fix a time. I'll see to it that she's home by then."

His face impassive, Ross suggested eleven o'clock, and Michael agreed without hesitation. Shortly after that he suggested that they leave. Anne said nothing on the way out, but once they stepped into the starry, crisp night, she said in a tight voice, "Michael, I won't have you manipulating me this way."

"I'd hardly call prompting you to do what you already agreed to do manipulating." His words carried a bite as astringent as the cold of the winter air.

She got into the car and started the engine almost before he climbed in beside her. With a hard jerk of the wheel, she set the vehicle in motion and drove out of the parking lot.

He asked, "Are you angry with me?"

Why did he seem suddenly insensitive to everything she felt? "What else would you expect me to be?"

"I don't know," he said in a curious tone. "You're so cool and controlled, I thought you were incapable of anger."

She threw him an incredulous look. "Is that how you see me? As some kind of—unfeeling robot?"

"Perhaps I did—a little," he mused, his words soft and thoughtful.

She glanced at him, hardly able to believe he meant it. But he wasn't smiling. She gripped the wheel and stared out into the night, feeling disturbed and—frightened. Beyond the beams of the car, the countryside was a rolling wash of white. The blue flare of a farmer's vapor lamp shone like a beacon from the top of a distant hill. Where was her beacon? Where was the lighthouse lamp that would keep her away from the shoals of her memories?

When she pulled up in front of his house, he reached for her, his mouth lowering toward hers.

"Don't," she said, giving him a little push with her hands. He withdrew at once. "I'll see you tomorrow then," he said, his words muffled as he opened the door and got out of the car.

Long, limber legs carried him up the walk. Then, perhaps because she had not put the car in gear, he turned. In the light of the porch his fair hair gleamed. He raised a hand in half-salute, half-farewell, and went into the house.

She sat for a moment longer, staring at the place on the porch where he had stood. Then she put the car in motion and drove home. It was only after she walked into the house that she realized she had driven through the streets unconsciously, without the slightest memory of doing so.

Inside the dark, silent house, she stood for a moment in the living room. The moon shone through the windows into the blue and turquoise world she had created and made it a dark, mysterious place where the glass sculptures sparkled in stray moonbeams. The discus thrower, his nude male body suspended in an agonizing contortion, dominated the room. She walked to the table and ran her hands over the muscles of his shoulders, the strength of his arms. The lines and corded strength were all there, but in cool glass rather than warm flesh. . . . She snatched her hand away and walked to the other side of the sofa to press the switch of the floor lamp. Away from its pool of light, her back to the discus thrower, she dropped into the opposite corner of its luxurious cushions—and waited.

Waited for the thoughts to come flooding in that she could no longer keep at bay. Waited for the memory of that last summer on the island. . . . She stared at the glass pitcher on the low table in front of her, remembering. . . .

The sounds came back first. The lap of the water against the shore, the screech of a gull, the almost artificial honk of a wild duck. Then the feel and texture of the Thousand Islands returned to her mind as she sat there. She slipped off her shoes and tucked her feet up under her, no longer resisting the memories. She remembered the smell of the water and the trees and the grass all mingled together and inevitably . . . Ross. . . .

He had arrived late that summer. She and her mother had been there for two weeks, and she had been going out of her mind with boredom. She was tired of going fishing and baiting her own hook, tired of swimming and not having to fend off Ross's attempts to duck her. Tired of sitting alone in the evening, missing their long, serious talks. She had tried to fill the hours, but her mother was poor company. Distracted and ill at ease in her daughter's presence, her mother seemed almost relieved when Anne took up a book and went down to the dock.

That afternoon, the big cruiser that belonged to Carson Leyton rounded the bend of the river. She threw down her book and stood at the edge of the dock, watching, her nerves tingling with anticipation. Ross had come.

In minutes the anchor splashed overboard and the dinghy came swinging down. Ross and his father were inside. She waved her arm in an arc over her head. Ross answered her wave, the sinewy muscles in his shoulders working as he lowered his hand to the oar and rowed the short distance to her. When they docked, Carson Leyton got out. He spoke to her and then asked her about her mother. She assured him that her mother was fine, and yes, she was at the cabin. Then Ross was there beside her, asking her to walk around the island with him, and she forgot Carson Leyton and gave Ross her joyful agreement. They meandered around the island, and she told him how glad she was to see him and how bored she had been without him. He seemed quieter, and she knew at once that the year had changed him. He looked more mature and adult than he had, even the previous summer. He was a man—with a man's appetites. The thought shocked her. She picked up a maple leaf and rubbed it between her fingers, feeling its wet, silky spines. . . .

"What have you got?" She looked up . . . and caught her

breath. His familiar gray eyes had an unfamiliar glitter in them. Her voice felt like sand in her throat. "Just a leaf. I was—feeling sorry for it—"

"Because it fell at the beginning of summer and not the end?"

She flashed a smile at him. "Yes. How did you know?"

The glitter became more intense, and then he looked away and up, as if he were extremely interested in the circling flight of a gull in the sky. In that long beat of time she watched him, mesmerized by the taut line of his throat left bare by his T-shirt. Her own throat seemed to close. Then he lowered his chin, and his eyes flickered over her, and the strange hunger in them disappeared. "Why shouldn't I know how you think?" he asked easily, a faint smile lifting his lips. "We've been—friends for a long time, haven't we?"

"Yes, of course," she said, and turned away to kick at a gnarled branch that was half buried under the earth at her feet, thinking that now that Ross was back, things would return to normal.

But they didn't. On their fishing trips, Ross was remote, cool. He stayed at one end of the powerboat, and positioned her at the other. If she moved near him, he moved away. He seemed to have developed an extreme abhorrence to any kind of physical contact with her. After years of horseplay with him, of the freedom to touch and be touched, her mind and body cried out in protest. At the end of a week, when his cool disdain hadn't altered, she took matters into her own hands.

They had fallen into the habit of going fishing in the early morning hours, when wisps of fog hung over the river and the sun was only a red glow below the horizon. She dressed and met him on the shore.

"Well, come on," he said brusquely, impatiently, saying the words without looking at her as he often had during the past week.

She walked out onto the dock, her feet making hollow sounds on the wooden boards. "No. I'm not going with you."

She had all his attention then. He stopped pulling at the wheel of the boat hoist and stared at her. "What do you mean you're not going."

She was two feet away from him on the dock. She lifted her chin to face him, like an opponent ready for battle. Against the red sky, he was a dark silhouette in his leather jacket, but she was close enough to see the angry, closed look on his face. "You go ahead," she told him, her voice as cool as the early morning breeze. "I'm sure you'll enjoy your own company more than you do mine."

"How do you know what I'll enjoy?" The question was half growled, barely leashed anger simmering in the words.

Her injured pride made her own anger bubble to the surface. "It's obvious, isn't it? You haven't had a civil word for me for days. You can't bear to be near me. Or touch me." Her knees trembled, but she kept her head high. "At least have the decency to be honest with me. Tell me I'm too young to interest your more—sophisticated tastes. . . ."

He let go of the wheel. The boat dropped with a splash into the water. Still partially tethered, it twisted inside the lines of the hoist and bumped the dock, the hollow sound echoing out over the water in the quiet of the morning. He lowered his arms slowly and took one step toward her. She had to brace herself and lock her knees to keep from backing away. "What do you know about my—sophisticated tastes?"

She couldn't back down. "Enough. I—"

Another lithe movement of his legs and he had reached her. "You don't know a damn thing about my tastes, but maybe it's time you learned. . . ."

The leather of his jacket creaking warned her. She took a step back and instinctively raised her hands, but it was far too late for defensive action. He gripped her shoulders and pulled her against him, his arms locking her lower body against his. He took her lips with a hard male assurance that was far beyond the

58

kisses she had exchanged with boys her age. She tried to push him away, but her hands on his chest were useless.

He lifted his head. "Stop fighting me, damn it." She hardly recognized that soft male growl as belonging to Ross. "You invited this. Open your mouth."

He held her in an iron grip, one hand cupping the back of her head. She couldn't move, couldn't breathe. His head came down again.

She made the mistake of saying no, and his mouth swooped and took what it had been denied, his tongue entering through the opening she had unwittingly provided. He explored the warm sweetness leisurely, taking his time, wooing her with light little flicks. Then, as her resistance melted and she tilted her head slightly to give him greater access, he rewarded her tentative yielding with bolder, longer strokes of his tongue, strokes that sent sensual tingles down to the bottom of her spine. She wriggled her hands away from their locked position against him and slid them around under his jacket to his back, conscious only of the driving urge to get closer, closer. . . .

A shudder racked his body. He lifted his head. His arms, which a moment ago had shackled her to him, fell away. "Now you know my tastes," he murmured. Their eyes locked and an aching silence vibrated between them. "Are you coming fishing with me?"

She shook her head, knowing that a morning spent as his fishing companion would be sheer torture.

A flash of pain crossed his face. "You're right, of course. I knew if I ever touched you, I'd lose you."

He turned away and stood looking out over the water, his back to her, his dark hair gleaming with a black-gold sheen in the sun's brighter rays. He looked vulnerable—and alone. And it was precisely at that moment she knew she loved him.

She crept up behind him and wrapped her arms around his waist, pressing her body against his back.

Every muscle in his body went hard with tension. "I'm warning you, Anne. I'm not a boy to be played with—to be kissed and teased and then told no."

"Would you like to be kissed and teased and then told yes?" she mocked softly.

"Stop it." An underlying agony made his voice harsh. "You don't know what you're saying."

She tugged on his arm until he turned toward her. "Darling Ross." She smiled up into his face, and it was a wise, womanly smile. "I may not be as old as you are, but I'm not a baby."

"You are," he grated. "Any twelve-year-old knows more about sex than you do. You've spent your life caressing piano keys."

Her temper flared. "And I'm too naive for you, is that it?"

He gritted his teeth and clenched his fists, and for one fleeting moment she thought he might hit her. "It won't work, Anne. You're not going to goad me into touching you again."

A thought churned up out of her fevered mind and, without thinking, she acted on it. "Then I'll touch you." She lifted her hands, and with a violent thrust, shoved him sideways. She would never have been so successful if he hadn't been as angry as she and already off-balance. And even then he could have saved himself by grabbing her arms. But he didn't. He reeled off the dock and fell into the water with a heavy splash. When he floundered for a moment and then surfaced in the deep water, she turned her back on him and walked away.

During the next few days she didn't see him. He kept well away from her, staying out on the cruiser at night, not even coming in for the dinner cooked by their excellent male chef at the cottage. She told herself she didn't care and practiced on the old upright in the living room, pounding the keys with her frustration, until her mother said one day, "Anne, for heaven's sake. Can't you play something soft? Chopin, Gottschalk, anything. That dreadful Brahms is getting on my nerves."

"Sorry, Mother." She got up from the piano and went upstairs. She knew she couldn't continue to sulk. She had to see him. She walked to her window and gazed at the cabin cruiser, wishing there were some way. . . . Inspiration struck and she tore off her clothes and got into her lime-green maillot.

She went out to the dock and dived into the river. A tiny waterproof packet tucked next to her breasts, she moved through the water in an easy, overhand crawl, not wanting to alert Ross to her approach. She reached the cruiser and, as quietly as she could, heaved herself up on the small rear platform. She lifted a slippery tan leg over the side—and was half in and half out of the boat when she heard a small noise. Then Ross's voice growled, "What the hell do you think you're doing?"

The shock of seeing him when she was so sure she hadn't been detected almost sent her over backward into the water. Then she gathered herself and swung her other leg over. "I'm coming to talk to you," she told him, trying to keep the defiant sound out of her words.

She flipped a long, heavy strand of hair away from her face and stared at him. He looked as if he hadn't shaved since the day she had pushed him in the lake—or eaten either, if it came to that. His clothes, a rumpled flannel shirt open to the waist and scruffy denims, looked as if he had been sleeping in them.

"What are you doing to yourself? You look awful."

He bowed his head in mocking acknowledgment. "Thank you." He lifted his head, and his eyes slid down her slick wet body. "And you look terrific. Now that we have the formalities out of the way—*get the hell off this boat.*"

She held up a pacifying hand and felt a complete fool when a drop of water slid down her elbow. She swiped at it with her other hand and said, "I'm not here to make you angry. I'm here to say I'm sorry about the other morning—and to give you this." She reached inside the bodice of her suit and brought out the small packet. It was several bills wrapped in plastic. "It's to help pay for the restoration of your ruined jacket. I know you won't be able to wear it again until you have it cleaned."

"I don't want your money," he told her, his voice tight.

"You accused me of acting like a child—and"—she lifted her chin—"you were right. Now, let me do the adult thing and at least make a partial contribution toward your cleaning bill."

She held it out to him, her eyes entreating him. "Please take it, Ross. Then I'll know that you've forgiven me." When she thought she could hold her breath no longer, he stretched out his hand. She placed the money on his palm, her eyes never leaving his face.

Her body crying for oxygen, she took a deep breath. "Well, I suppose I'd better be going."

She pivoted to climb back over the side, praying he wouldn't let her go. He didn't. "Anne." The husky tremor in his voice gave her the first spark of hope.

"Yes?" She turned, her face carefully blank.

"Would you—like some coffee?"

She smiled. "As a peace offering?"

He shrugged. "If you'd like to think of it as that—yes." A tiny smile tugged at his mouth. "I might even shave for the occasion."

"All right," she said, smiling.

"You'll need this." He picked up a towel from one of the deck chairs and tossed it to her.

"Thanks." He didn't turn away as she wrapped the towel around her body and tucked the ends in above her breasts. She was conscious of his gaze on her every moment, and when she raised her eyes to his, her breath seemed to catch in her throat at the expression in those gray depths.

With a muffled exclamation that meant nothing—or everything—he turned and went down the steps, his black head disappearing below the hatch.

CHAPTER FOUR

"Anne, for heaven's sake. Someone's at the door. Are you going to answer it, or shall I?"

The past faded from her mind. Still seated on the couch, she stared up at Shari. The girl was on the stairs, leaning over the banister, a frown wrinkling her brow, the hall light giving her loose dark hair a satin sheen. She had evidently thrown her robe over her sleep shirt. Jeff Overholzer's number, fifty-four, was emblazoned on the red-and-white material under the edges. The robe didn't conceal the way Shari's small, high breasts pushed against the cotton fabric. She must have been reading. Her hated glasses were perched on the bridge of her nose, making her look appealing and attractive in a little-girl-grown-big way.

"Someone's been leaning on the doorbell for the last five minutes." Shari took another step and grimaced as the chime sounded again.

"It's just someone to see me. Go back to your studying, Shari." She got up from the couch, trying to keep her voice cool and noncommittal. The last thing she wanted to do was arouse her sister's curiosity. But it was too late. Anne knew from the expression on Shari's face that she was already intrigued.

"Who's coming to see you at this hour of the night? Michael?" The dark feminine eyebrows arched in a questioning line.

"No, it's not Michael. Do go upstairs, Shari. You're hardly dressed to receive anyone."

The doorbell went again, and she turned away and walked down the hall, thinking that Shari would take the hint and disappear upstairs.

She opened the door and thoughts of Shari were thrust from her mind. Snow had begun to swirl in the air, and behind Ross the sky was dark and filled with drifting snowflakes. A few lay sprinkled on his black hair. For a moment, seeing them nestled in the satin strands, she wanted to reach up and brush them away. His slow smile brought her back to reality. Dear God, could he know what she was thinking?

She said, "Come in," and stepped back, despising herself for the sudden throatiness of her voice as he moved into the narrow hall beside her.

She pivoted and moved ahead of him into the living room, her legs working by some power not connected to her processes of thought. To her utter disbelief and greater displeasure, she saw that Shari had not moved from her spot halfway up the stairs.

Shari saw the caller, smiled brightly, and took the remaining five steps that brought her to the floor of the living room directly in front of Ross. "Hi." Her robe dangling around her knees, her bare toes curled into the carpet, there was a mixture of young-girl shyness and knowledge old as Eve in the face she turned up to Ross Leyton.

Anne felt a pang of annoyance. Ross, however, was gravely courteous. "Hello."

"You're Ross Leyton, aren't you?"

Anne winced at Shari's typical directness, but Ross only smiled a slow smile and inclined his head. Anne's annoyance heightened. Why hadn't she sent her sister to her room when the doorbell rang the first time? Why had she been foolish enough

64

to run the risk of exposing her young sister to Ross Leyton's practiced charm?

"And you're Shari." His voice was smooth, lacking the condescension adults sometimes used when meeting a teenager for the first time.

Shari beamed. "Yes." She shot a triumphant look at Anne. "How did you know?"

A quirk of amusement tipped the corners of Ross's mouth. "Process of elimination."

Shari tipped her head slightly to one side. "My mother hasn't told you about me?"

"Yes," Ross admitted, "she has. But her information is dated. She remembers you as a little girl"—he smiled as his eyes traveled over her—"not as the young woman you are now."

Attractive color bloomed in Shari's cheeks under the creamy skin. "How—how is my mother?"

There was a slight pause, as if Ross had to consider a careful answer to the prosaic question. He glanced at Anne's cool face and then said easily, "She's reasonably well."

"I'm glad," Shari told him, missing the hesitant quality in the words. "Do you see her often?"

"Not as often as I'd like."

"Let me take your coat," Anne interrupted, throwing a dark glance at her sister, her voice impersonally polite. "Would you like a drink?"

"No, thank you." He glanced at Anne. "The wine we had at dinner was enough."

Shari shot Anne a fierce look. "I thought you were going out with Michael." Her voice had a brittle sound.

"I happened to run into your sister while I was out dining with my assistant." He smiled as he gently appeased her. Anne only became more annoyed. "Had I known you were home alone," he continued to Shari, "you certainly would have been invited to join us."

Slightly mollified, Shari turned to Anne and said, "Well,

aren't you going to invite him to sit down, for heaven's sake, or are we just going to stand here at the foot of the stairs all evening?"

Anne bit back several sharp retorts that occurred to her and said, "Yes, of course," waving a hand in the general direction of the sofa.

Ross settled himself into one corner. To Anne's complete chagrin, Shari sat down next to him. "I hardly think it's fair that Anne gets a chance to get reacquainted with you—and I don't."

Anne fought the urge to tell her to close her robe and moved to sit in the chair at the end of the couch, her teeth clenched, her body cold. If Ross said anything about their mother wanting a visit, he would be gaining a powerful ally. She could almost see the thought flicker across his face—and be rejected. Oh, dear God, why, in ten years, did she still have the ability to know what he was thinking and feeling? She was still so in tune with him, she could read the lift of his eyebrow, the tightening of his lips, like the signs on a map. Why in ten years hadn't she forgotten the way their thoughts always seemed to trail each other like railroad cars on a track?

"I won't be leaving Runford for a few days, Shari. Would you care to have dinner with me one evening?"

Her stomach muscles knotted convulsively. She couldn't stop the betraying movement of her hand to her middle. Shari's back was to her, but Ross didn't miss that slight movement. "The invitation includes your sister, too, of course."

Shari made a dissatisfied sound, while Anne's thoughts tumbled in a frantic effort to keep hold of her sanity. If she refused the invitation, she would leave the field free for Ross to feed Shari's rapidly developing infatuation for him. If she didn't refuse, she would be subjected to watching him ply his charm on Shari for an entire evening. But being there was infinitely better than not being there.

"Yes, we must do that." Anne forced the words from her throat.

Ross smiled at Shari. "Let's set a night, shall we? Since tomorrow evening is the recital, how does Saturday sound?" Ross's smile widened. "Unless you already have a date . . ."

Shari shook her head quickly, her dark hair flying. "Saturday night is super."

"Good." Ross's smile was charming, persuasive. "Now, I need some time to talk to your sister alone, honey." He reached up his hand and pushed back the glasses on the bridge of her nose. "Don't you have some homework to do?"

"Anne and I don't have any secrets from each other," she protested. "Please let me stay." Shari had her own beguiling ways, but Ross shook his head. "You and I are not quite on those same terms," he said, "and what I have to say is for your sister's ears alone."

The words were firm. He let the silence grow and sat back, subtly sending the message that he knew she was a reasonable young woman and would do what he wanted her to do. She studied his face and realized there was nothing she could do but give in gracefully. She got to her feet. "Well, I'll say good night, then. I'll see you Saturday." She crossed to the bottom of the stairs, but with her hand on the banister, she pivoted around to face Ross. "What shall I wear?"

"Something gorgeous," he answered without hesitation.

She flashed him a brilliant smile and began to climb the stairs. "Terrific. I'll see you then."

She bounded gracefully up the remainder of the stairs, and when she had disappeared from sight, Anne sat frozen in her chair by the mixture of relief and fear that coursed through her. She was glad that Shari was away from Ross's presence for the moment, but she was none too eager to be left alone with him.

Restlessly she moved in her chair. Her own sense of fairness made her say, "Thank you for not involving her in this."

His face was shadowed as he leaned back against the couch, and for once she couldn't read his cool expression. "The decision has to be yours. *Have* you changed your mind?"

Her voice was low. "Yes."

He didn't move from his relaxed position, and if there was triumph in his face, she couldn't see it. He crossed one leg casually over the other at the knee and said, in that low voice she had never quite forgotten, "Your change of mind doesn't seem to be motivated by a change of heart. May I ask just exactly why you are saying yes now when your no was so adamant only this afternoon?"

She clenched her teeth and told herself to get this over with quickly. "Father contributed to the Runford Music School each year—a sum of fifteen thousand dollars. I'll go to visit my mother, if you agree to continue the practice."

An ominous silence settled in the room. He sat staring at her for so long, she thought he was going to refuse. Instead, he said softly, "I can't believe this is your idea."

Inwardly she winced, but outwardly she kept her face impassive. "Is it so hard to believe that the school means a great deal to me?"

He uncrossed his legs and got to his feet. Slowly he walked toward her, his relaxed attitude gone. There was the stalking menace of a lean, predatory jaguar in the smooth way he advanced on her. She drew back into the cushion of the chair, but his arm shot out and he hauled her to her feet.

She gasped and struggled to free herself from those cool fingers on her arm, but he held her easily. "I think I must have idolized you over the years." His eyes glittered over her stiff face. "I would never have believed the warm, loving girl I knew was capable of such cold-blooded scheming."

A harsh, quick laugh bubbled out of her throat. "You and my mother taught me well. You can hardly blame me if I return the same kind of consideration I got from both of you."

His jaw tightened. "I knew you wouldn't be disposed to think kindly of me, but don't take that out on Leora—"

"*Think kindly of you!* I loathe and despise you!" She fired the words at him, words that burned inside her with white-hot flames.

He pulled her closer until his lean length burned down hers. "There were circumstances, things that happened that summer that made it impossible for me to get in touch with you again. There was a misunderstanding . . ."

"You mean the circumstances of my mother having an affair with your father?" She stared at him, her eyes blazing. "I have some respect for him at least. He stood by my mother. He married her. He didn't let her wait and wonder and hope and wish and dream . . ."

"Anne—"

"Let go of my arm." The crisp, cool words didn't seem to be coming from her throat. They had little effect on Ross. His grip tightened.

Anne said, "Is your answer yes or no?" She was desperate to get this whole horrible business over with, desperate to remove herself from his compelling male presence and escape those hard fingers on her arm, which only made her want more.

His hand dropped away. "Yes. I accept your terms." His face was bleak, unreadable.

She fought her own emotional response to that low, agonized tone. "I want it put in writing."

A muscle moved on the side of his jaw. "That won't be necessary."

She couldn't weaken, not now with victory so close. "I'll have a lawyer draw up something and have it to you by the day after tomorrow," she told him, contradicting his statement. "No travel arrangements can be made until both you and I have signed the document." How utterly callous she sounded. But it was the only way. She had to close off her own feelings—if she was to see this through.

"Anne, for God's sake—"

"No," she said, hating the cold sound of her voice. "I want

everything done on a businesslike basis." She held his eyes, daring him. "That way there'll be no—misunderstanding."

He stared at her, his dark-gray eyes almost black with anger. "I believe a better term would be *cash basis.*"

She reeled from his harsh condemnation but somehow managed to keep her face from revealing her inner turmoil. "Call it anything you like. The fact remains that I want a signed contract with Western Data before Shari and I step one foot out of this house."

She waited, watching him, suddenly aware that he had become a cold stranger. She remembered him as a warm, teasing companion. But that was ten years ago, and ten years is a long time. She no longer knew him, not really. The rapport she had felt with him moments ago must have been an illusion. She was facing a man, a mature, powerful man who was the head of a large conglomerate, a man whose decisions affected the lives of thousands of people. He spent days and weeks and months in meetings and offices, manipulating and maneuvering, undoubtedly becoming much more adept at it than she.

His anger seemed to linger in the air like lightning, and its existence was so real, she thought for a moment he was going to lose control and reach out to her to grasp her and shake her. But he didn't. "You'll have it." He reached around her to gather up his coat from the back of her chair, a sardonic smile flickering over his lips as she flinched involuntarily. "Good night. I'll see you at the recital tomorrow evening. Don't bother to see me out. I know the way." With a mocking bow of his head, he pivoted and strode down the hall, closing the door behind him softly. For some reason it disturbed her more than any violent slamming could have. There was, in that silent closing, the subtle, menacing promise of things to come.

A few minutes later, upstairs, she crept into her room to avoid confronting Shari and shut her door to lean against it and try to quiet the pounding of her heart. She had won. Ross had agreed to her demands. The worst was over.

Is it? her mind mocked. *Listen to your heart. It's pounding like a drum after twenty minutes with him. How will you survive whole days in his company?*

You must limit the time to a week, she thought frantically. *Only a week—*

A counter melody played the thought back. *How will that save you? You were with him less than a week up at the Islands. . . .*

She undressed and got into bed, lying stiff and unrelaxed between the sheets. If only she had swum away from the boat the first time that day! If only she hadn't stayed and drunk his coffee and assured him that it was very good. . . . She could almost hear his low, husky voice saying . . .

"How's the coffee?"

He had shaved and changed and now was seated across from her in the cozy dining nook under the deck. He leaned back against the velvet cushion tucked in the corner of the seat and waited for her answer.

She smiled. "Excellent. You'll make some woman a wonderful husband."

She expected a smile, but instead a frown drew his brows together. A curious little silence fell between them, and self-consciously aware that she had somehow blundered, she averted her eyes from his and ran a fingertip around the handle of the white mug he had given her.

But she soon lost interest in the mug and glanced back up at him. He seemed lost in his own thoughts, a brooding look on his face. He had changed into white chino pants and a white shirt that hung open and exposed hard, tan flesh and dark curls of hair on the flat, muscular chest. The cream leather bench, mahogany paneling, and pastel watercolor behind his dark head were a luxurious backdrop that made him seem more primitive and male than ever.

She plucked up her courage and gave him a careless smile.

71

"I—I've changed my mind about—fishing. Could we plan to go out tomorrow morning?"

He seemed to still his body, as if bracing himself. "No."

"Why not?" The words sounded suitably casual, careless, but his eyes flickered away in what was, for Ross, an uncharacteristic refusal to meet hers. "I'm leaving tomorrow."

The swift rise of tears made her look down. "Because of me?"

In the silence, the boat rocked gently. When he didn't answer, she looked up at him and found that he was examining her with sharp, watchful eyes. Not caring that the tears were there for him to see, she said, "It's true, isn't it?"

His mouth tightened. "Yes, it's true." He hesitated and then reached out to cover her hand with his. "Anne, for God's sake, try to understand."

She said fiercely, "Oh, I understand all right. I understand that just because you accepted my apology, and plied me with coffee, it doesn't mean that anything's changed. The message is still the same. *You want me out of your life!*" She snatched her hand from his and brushed her eyes with it. "Well, you can stop worrying, Mr. Leyton. I won't bother you again—*ever!*"

She pushed herself off the leather seat and got to her feet to make her escape, but he was too quick for her. He was out of his seat and blocking her path before she had taken a step, his arms catching her in a vise grip. "Anne, don't let us part this way."

She struggled for a moment, her fury making her wild. Then the thought penetrated her brain that she was where she wanted to be, in his arms. She stopped struggling and let the sensations of wild excitement tingle through her. "Ross," she murmured, burying her head in his shoulder, "oh, Ross . . ." She lay there with his hard body against the softness of hers, suddenly aware that he was as disturbed as she. His heart was pounding against her breasts. A powerful surge of happiness coursed through her. She raised her head, her mouth curved in a joyous smile . . . until she saw his face. It was stony.

"Ross," she pleaded, and ever afterward she was to remember that supplication in her voice. "Please make love to me, Ross. I want to belong to you. I *do,* anyway. I always have."

He didn't flicker an eyelash. His gaze was cool and steady. "No." The words was flat and hard. "No."

"Are you trying to convince me—or yourself?" She traced a fingertip around the outer part of his ear and felt him tremble in response.

With a bold audaciousness she didn't know she had, she leaned forward and touched her tongue to the lobe of his ear. She explored it with her lips, her tongue, her teeth, biting him gently. He shuddered—but he didn't push her away. He seemed immobilized by her sensual exploration of his ear, an exploration that was widening to include the side of his cheek, the corner of his mouth.

"If it will make you feel better," she goaded softly, "give me your lecture now about how I'm too young for you, and how I have to concentrate on my promising career"—she punctuated each phrase with a kiss on his unresponsive mouth—"and how I don't really know what I'm doing"—her tongue probed between his lips—"and we'll have that all over with." She breathed the words into his mouth.

"There's one more thing you might add to your little list of things I'd lecture you on," he said. His hands grasped her shoulders and he put her away from him. "I might remind you that part of being a real woman is letting the man think it's his idea." Cold fury permeated his voice. "Now, take your little seductive tricks—*and get out of here!*"

An intolerable pain exploded inside her. She brushed past him, ran up the steps, and took the second set of stairs at full tilt, to burst out of the hatch onto the deck.

The dull thud of her feet across the deck registered in her brain, but she didn't consciously think about running to the edge and jumping over the side. She only realized she had done it when the water shocked her overheated body. And she didn't consciously think about staying under. She simply didn't fight her way to the surface like she normally would. What difference did it make what she did?

She let herself drift in the underwater world, ignoring the bursting feeling in her lungs. For down here was an escape from pain, a shelter to hide in. . . . She drifted on in the sea-green world in a wonderful state of numbness. Time seemed to stand still, to float with her . . . until she would find a place in the river to hide in forever. . . . Hard hands caught her arm. She was hauled upward with a ruthless force she couldn't fight.

Her head was lifted above the water, and her back felt the relentless pounding of a large, heavy hand. "Breathe, damn you. Breathe!"

She did, only because it seemed less painful to do as she was told rather than to feel another blow from that hand. Ross was holding her, his fingers like iron clamps on her shoulders.

"You're hurting me," she protested.

With ruthless dispatch, he hauled her toward the boat and gave her a scathing look. "You're lucky I don't kill you. Get your feet up there."

He bent her knees and propped her up on the back projection on the boat. Then, with a very ungentle hand on her bottom, he pushed her face forward into the boat. She fell to her hands and knees, aching, angry.

When she heard Ross move in behind her, she scrambled to her feet. His words exploded around her.

"My God! You're ten times a bigger fool than I thought you were!"

The urge to wound him was overpowering. "I must be," she said, her voice hoarse. "Because I was ten times the fool to fall in love with you."

She didn't have time to see his reaction. Nausea rose in her throat and sent her fighting to reach the side of the boat in time.

He let her system find relief, and when the crisis had passed, he took her arm and led her to a chair to press her into it. He left her, and she made a small sound of protest. He was back beside her immediately. From somewhere he had found a clean damp towel and wiped her mouth and face. She sat like a child, letting him minister to her, dazed by his sudden change in attitude. He hadn't bothered to dry himself with a towel. His lashes were spiky with moisture from his dive into the river, and his shirt was soaked and clinging with what must have been uncomfortable wetness to his chest and back. His pants, too, were sodden.

When she had recovered somewhat, he knelt down beside her chair and laid his dark head against her wet thigh. Her head came finally to rest against his shoulder. As if from a great distance he said, "Don't ever do that to me again."

How long they sat there like that, just touching, making human contact with each other but saying nothing, she couldn't tell. At last he rose. "Come below," he said gently. "I'll get you something to wear and take you home in the dinghy."

He went ahead of her, guiding her down the hatch stairs with her hand in his and led the way to the tiny bedroom tucked under the front of the boat. She was deposited just inside the door. He turned his back to her and began to rummage through a built-in chest of drawers. "You can wear one of my shirts and a pair of my denims with a belt, I think."

As if she were in a dream, her hands moved to the top of her suit. She stripped it down over her hips and stepped out of it. "Ross." Her voice was husky.

He turned.

She held her head high, knowing that she had invited his eyes to have their pleasure of her. Ross took his time, letting his gaze travel over the rose-tipped breasts, the flat stomach, the long, silken thighs.

"If you tell me to get dressed—and leave you—I will," she said softly.

He stood stock-still, like a man in shock. His eyes roamed over her silken flesh, from the creamy shoulders to the slender ankles.

75

He seemed to be drinking in the essence of her, as if he had been starved for her. But he didn't move. She could almost feel the tension in his body as he strained to keep from stepping toward her. Boldly she moved toward him and reached out to brush the wet shirt away from his chest. An almost inhuman sound came from his throat. He tossed the clothes on the floor and pulled her into his arms.

"For years," he muttered, "I've been watching you, wondering what you'd be like when you became a woman, wanting to be the man who made you one. . . ." His lips came down on hers with a fierce, aching passion that demanded as it possessed, took as it asked. She had thought he would take his time with her, wooing her gently to allow for her inexperience. He allowed for nothing. The hard, insistent probe of his tongue explored the inner recesses of her mouth while his hands sought the long, exquisitely sensitive curve of her back.

He lowered her to the bed, and she felt the brush of the expensive soft silk against her back. "Ross—the spread. My hair is wet."

"Damn the spread," he murmured with a husky intensity that thrilled her. "We'll send it in with my jacket." Husky amusement lurked in the words.

With gentle fingertips he explored her, tracing a teasing path between her breasts, lingering over the wildly beating pulse at her throat. When his hand wandered lower to the soft curve of her breast and his fingers took its weight, her heart seemed to pound in her ears. Never before had a man's hand explored the ruby tip. Never before had a man's hand smoothed over the flat surface of her belly, circled around the indentation of her navel, or discovered the soft and delicious curve of her thighs. When she moaned and moved as if to escape him, the sweet agony of his touch more than she could bear, he leaned over her and murmured into her mouth, "You're courageous and warm and loving beyond belief. You don't think I'd let you leave me now, do you? My blood's on fire for you, woman."

76

And she was a woman, a woman who shared the desire she felt in his hands, his mouth. Under his fingertips, she was elemental, primitive, a woman claiming her lover after years of deprivation. She let her hands move over his body, the smooth skin still damp from his plunge into the river to save her. Delight converged under her fingertips at the feel of him, the hard, corded muscles of his back, the rounded firmness of his buttocks. The instinct to claim him as her own made her rake her nails gently up his spine and feel his shuddering response with an acute sense of pleasure. She caressed his nape, and the crisp aliveness of his hair was another sensual satisfaction to the palms of her hands.

But while her fingers were making their journey over him, his were discovering her. His mouth nibbled around her breast, his tongue teasing and enticing. She shivered, waiting for the moment he would claim her taut peak with his mouth. He laughed softly. "Is something wrong?"

"No . . ." He was tantalizing her, building a fire in her blood to match his own. "Oh, Ross . . ."

"Sweet, oh, God, you're sweet—as sweet as I knew you would be. . . ."

He bent his head, pressing his mouth against her warm stomach. His hands moved over her slender thighs. The onslaught on her senses went on, carried to every inch of her body. Not a particle of her escaped his loving attention. He kissed the roundness of her knees, discovered the brown smoothness of her legs, caressed the sensitive bones of her ankles.

"Ross—" An unaccountable shyness swept over her. She wasn't afraid for herself, she was afraid that she would seem inexperienced to him, and that she wouldn't be able to pleasure him as he was pleasuring her. . . .

"Shh . . ." His mouth moved against her breast.

She said softly to his bent head, "I—want this to be right for you. . . ."

The lean face raised to her, its lines twisted in a paroxysm of emotion. What had she done? She reached up and touched his mouth with a gentle questing fingertip. He groaned and buried his head against her naked breast in a strange gesture of loving humbleness that made her heart soar with relief. After a long moment, he said in a husky, disturbed tone, "*You are* everything that is right. But this shouldn't be happening—now."

She kissed his tortured eyes, feeling his lashes under her lips. "There's no going back," she murmured.

He buried his mouth in the delicate hollow of her neck. "No," he said, "there's no going back." His mouth moved to her breast and at last he gave her the caress she craved. He took her rosy crest into his mouth, bringing her body to a new, fevered height of need. But the torture had only begun. His hands wandered lower, discovering her femininity. The sweet, forbidden caresses quickened her breathing, made her skin burn. An explosion of desire set off a chain reaction, forcing her to clutch his arms and arch her body toward him.

His hands played a sweeter music, his eyes never leaving her face. There was a gentle persuasion in his loving touch, a burning desire in his eyes, and such tenderness in the way he was holding her that in that moment, she knew he was the supreme lover she had dreamed him to be. She moaned and twisted, forgetting everything, knowing only that she had been born to exist for this moment, that she belonged to Ross and always would. She was caught between wanting his hands to orchestrate this melody forever . . . and aching for the crescendo to begin that would make her his.

"Ross—please—make me yours. I want to belong to you."

At last he headed her pleadings and moved over her. She clutched his shoulders and sought his warm, salty skin with her mouth. He groaned and kissed her, taking her lips with passion while his hard body sought the softness of hers. With consummate skill he made them one. She gasped at the pain and cried out at the pleasure. It was too much, this feeling of utter joy, of belonging. Another gasp of sheer ecstasy escaped her, and as if he, too, shared her desire to cry out her love, his mouth clamped down on hers, and his tongue gained entrance. His possession of her was complete. . . .

Even after they floated down from the heights, he lay beside her, extending her pleasure by tracing an idle circle around her breast. She watched his tan hand move against the paleness of her skin with a curious satisfaction, a feeling of belonging. "Ross." It seemed to take all her effort to talk. She felt languid, sated.

"Umm?" His finger continued its slow, provocative circling, making sensual pleasure linger deep within her.

"Do you think we were once lovers in Ancient Rome—or Babylonia?"

He raised up on his elbow and smiled down at her, a slow, wicked smile. "Do you see us having orgies under a grapevine?"

She took a deep breath and marshaled her courage to say, "It doesn't matter what we were in the past, does it? The future is what matters."

Her eyes searched his face. His bland expression gave no sign of his thoughts. His mouth was relaxed, his eyes half-hooded with dark lashes.

When she could stand his lack of reaction no longer, she asked hesitantly, "*Do* we have a future together, Ross?"

He stared at her for a long moment. Then he lowered his head and caressed her nipple with his tongue. Huskily, against her skin, he said, "Are you asking me to marry you?"

It was difficult to think clearly with his warm mouth making that pink bud harden with desire. "I—I suppose I am."

He seemed to ponder the thought. "You're not even of age. We'd need parental consent."

That he had thought of it sent a thrill of hope through her. "But we've known each other for years. My mother thinks you're marvelous. Why would that be a problem?"

He moved closer and favored her other breast with the sensual attention he had given the first. "How can you be sure you want to spend the rest of your life with me? You're very young. You've seen almost nothing of the world."

"I don't want to see the world." She lifted her hand to caress the dark hairs at his nape as he bent over her. "I only want to be with you."

"You're too young to know that."

"What a tiresome refrain you play," she said dryly. He was openly caressing her with his mouth and hands, purposely arousing her. "I certainly seem to be old enough for—one aspect of marriage, at least."

He blew lightly over her breast, sending shivers of delight quivering over her skin. "I can't argue with that."

"Well . . . ?"

His hands began the rhapsody once again. "Let me give it some thought."

She touched her tongue to the hard cord at the side of his throat. "And have you thought of something we can do while you're thinking?"

"Yes," he muttered softly. "Yes."

In the end she dressed in his clothes and he took her home. He helped her out of the dinghy into the pale twilight. They stood on the shore of the island, like strangers who couldn't find the right words.

"I'll be leaving tomorrow as I planned," he said, the words like tiny needles of pain.

"No. Please don't do that."

"I must," he said coolly. "You have to have some time to think this through—time away from me. If you still feel the same way in a year—"

"No! Six weeks," she said firmly. "When I have my eighteenth birthday."

"Anne, for God's sake, be reasonable." Exasperation crackled through his voice. "You'll still be in high school."

"I don't care," she said blithely. "I can finish school in California after we're married. I'll call on October twenty-first"—she laughed up in his somber face—"and fly out to you on the twenty-second."

He pulled her close and kissed her with a fierce passion. "I must be out of my mind even to let you consider it." His dark hair lifted in the slight breeze as he held her away and gazed down at her. "Anne," he said soberly, "be very sure. Because once we're married, there's no way I could ever let you go."

And she had believed him! *She had believed him!*

She raised herself up and pounded her pillow in an agony of humiliation, remembering how, on the day of her birthday, she had got out of bed, scarcely able to breathe with excitement, knowing that this was the day she would be talking to Ross, hearing his voice, making plans to be with him.

She waited with great impatience for the afternoon to come so that she could make her call—only to be told by his secretary that he was in conference and that he would call her as soon as he was finished. She waited by the phone, confident that he would call back within the hour. All that afternoon she waited—and into the evening, until twelve o'clock that night. . . .

She went to bed at last, knowing it was a simple mistake. It had to be. He just hadn't got her message.

But at the end of five days of trying to reach him, the truth sank in. No secretary could be blamed for his silence.

He had decided he didn't want to marry her.

Once started, the devastating thoughts continued in a relentless procession that tore and ripped at her soul. He had never wanted to marry her. He had been putting her off with his talk of her youth, and the seriousness of commitment to him. Irony twisted her mouth. He had had his excuses all ready. Now, with the clarity of thought afforded by the greater distance, she began to understand why he had left her so abruptly, why he had insisted that she call him, why he had wanted her to wait for a year. He had planned it all quite cleverly, really, letting her exist on her little bit of hope until finally his secretary would take even that away. . . . Her mother left the next week.

CHAPTER FIVE

That next evening, sitting with her father in the small pub, surrounded by noisy people and the smell of crisply fried fish and potatoes, she knew this was what she needed to drive thoughts of Ross from her mind, the sounds and sights and smells of the real world. There was pleasure in watching Tom Wheeler drinking from his glass stein and lowering it to the table with a solid chunk, pleasure in seeing the familiar flush on Mary's face as she worked behind the bar, almost running to keep up with the orders.

There was hardly anyone seated at the round wooden tables she didn't know. She had been coming here with her father on Friday nights since the time her mother had left them.

She sat back in her chair, pushed the cardboard container with its small mound of crispy potatoes away, and wiped her fingers on her napkin. "As always, it was delicious. Thank you, Father."

He lifted a glass of wine toward her, but his eyes were guarded above it. "As always . . . it was my pleasure." He closed his eyes and tilted the glass, his throat moving as he drank. Gray strands gleamed in his fair hair, almost eclipsing the dark gold.

He set his glass on the table, loosened his tie, and unbuttoned the top button of his white shirt. His dark blue suit looked rumpled, and there were weary lines beside his mouth. He had obviously had a difficult day. Her heart went out to him.

"I didn't hear you come in last night," he said, looking at her thoughtfully. "Were you out late with Michael?"

"I—came in early." She sipped her own wine, hoping her father would not pursue his line of questioning. There was no reason he should. He had long ago given up keeping watch on her late-night hours.

Carefully, still watching her, he said, "You must not have slept too well after you got in. You've got dark circles under your eyes."

She tried a light laugh. "You can't possibly see them from over there in this place," she parried. "It must be your imagination."

He twisted his glass on the table. "I don't think it's my imagination that you've been unusually quiet this evening. Are you upset about—the merger?"

She kept her voice bland. "No. I—I realize that it was something you felt you had to do, and that it's probably the right thing for everybody involved. I can accept that. It's just that I've got a lot on my mind—with the recital and all . . ."

"Ah, yes, the recital." His tone of voice told her he knew she was prevaricating. But he only said, "I'm looking forward to it."

She let her lips curve into a smile. Her father was a frustrated musician who loved to watch the students perform. If Anne was playing on the program as the faculty soloist, he preened himself like a young peacock as he sat watching her.

"So it's the recital that's putting that serious look on your face—not the fact that you've agreed to see your mother." He sat back, well aware that he had thrown a bomb at her head.

She held his gaze, but the color rose in her cheeks. "Ross told you." She was upset about that. She had planned to tell him herself, tonight.

He nodded. "This morning, when we were touring the plant."

At the dark frown she gave him, he said quickly, "Don't blame Ross. I asked him point-blank if you had come to an agreement."

For the first time she realized that her father, for some mysterious reason, *wanted* her to make this trip. It was beyond her comprehension. In his place, she would probably have felt betrayed. "Father, you know my feelings for you will never change, don't you?"

His eyebrows flew up in a startled grimace. Color appeared in his cheeks, probably from the wine he had been drinking. "Of course I do."

His reaction seemed so intense. She said carefully, "You seem very anxious for this grand . . . family reunion to take place."

His hand covered hers on the table. He gazed at her, as if he were groping for the words he wanted to say. "I have to admit I was—very bitter when I found out that Leora had been—seeing another man. But you're old enough now to try to understand— and forgive a little."

She was filled with irrational anger. "How can you sit there and defend her? She left you to marry a wealthy man."

"But—it cost her. Dearly. She lost you . . . and Shari."

Hotly she retorted, "That was her choice."

"Not entirely . . ."

"What do you mean, not entirely? She told me there was no place for us in her life."

"Anne—"

"Don't," she said huskily. "I won't go through with this at all if you champion her case along with—along with everyone else. I'll go to see her, but that's all. She'll never become a part of my life." Her voice trembled with vehemence.

"But there's something you don't know, something I—"

"It doesn't matter." She felt battered, wrecked upon the reefs of reliving the past. "It all happened a long time ago and nothing we do now can change it."

A strange, almost relieved look flickered over his face. "Anne,

I want you to know that I'm—I'm glad you—you have no regrets. Just promise me that you'll be—civil to your mother."

She frowned darkly, and he raised his hand in a pleading gesture. "Please, Anne. It will ease my—ease things. I've always regretted the fact that you were alienated from your mother at the time of your life that—she went away. I—I hadn't realized that you would take it so hard."

There was a sudden outburst of laughter from the table behind them. Anne started, and the color drained away from her face. It took her a moment to collect her poise. Then she relaxed slightly and said, "There were other—other circumstances that contributed to my—bitterness about my mother."

She glanced up and found him gazing at her with an odd, almost tortured look in his eyes. Then he caught up his glass and said hastily, "Well, as you say, it's all in the past. Let's drink to the future, shall we?"

An hour later, at the music school, she thought of the drink she had shared with her father when she poured the cherry-colored, nonalcoholic punch into the punch bowl. She finished her task and carried the empty cans into the kitchen. When she stepped back out into the double living room, she was filled with a sense of satisfaction. Her life, the future that she had drunk to with her father, was here. Rows of chairs facing the baby grand piano sat empty and waiting. A cake decorated with a music staff, a treble clef, and the name of the school in dark blue frosting was positioned next to the punch bowl for everyone to admire before it was cut. Around the edges, Karen had painstakingly outlined the students' names in pink. A bouquet of red carnations added color to the table. At the end of the recital she would present a flower to each of the relieved participants. There would be twelve of them, six pianists, four violinists, and two little boys who were Michael's students who played half-size cellos.

At seven thirty she stood at the door to welcome the performers and their families as they came in—and wondered where he was. Most of the students had filled their assigned seats in the first two rows only minutes later, and Michael still had not appeared.

She was just getting ready to go and call him when he breezed in the entryway. Balancing his cello case on the floor, he brushed the snow from the front of his tweed jacket. Jane trailed in behind him, her violin case tucked under her arm, as if it were a part of her.

Karen handed him a program. "Car trouble, Mr. Adams?" The young girl's mouth twisted in a grimace.

Michael's long fingers began restlessly tapping on the top of his case as he stood waiting for Jane to remove her coat. He seemed disconcerted about something—perhaps about the fact that he was late. "What else? I was walking over when Jane took pity on me and gave me a lift."

One of Karen's well-shaped eyebrows lifted. "What a lucky coincidence." The words held a sardonic undertone that was puzzling.

But whatever it was that was upsetting Karen, Anne knew they didn't have time to discuss it now. "Your music stands are set up in my office," she said to him. "Robert and Tricia are waiting there for you to tune."

Michael leaned over and kissed her cheek with a careless brush of his mouth. "You're so efficient and organized, my love. What would I do without you?" He picked up his cello.

"Yes," Karen agreed, her voice soft but biting. "You wouldn't want to be—out of tune with the other members of your quartet, would you, Mr. Adams?"

He gave her a black glance and then said "Come on" to Jane and strode out of the anteroom with Jane trailing after him.

Anne turned to find Karen staring at her with a strange look on her face. "What was that all about?" she asked, feeling a vague disquiet. Karen was normally an enthusiastic, warm girl with an easy way that made her excellent in her job.

Instantly a polite mask replaced the almost unpleasant expression on the girl's face. "Nothing. He just—gets on my nerves, that's all."

"I didn't think anything bothered you," Anne said coolly.

"Well, *he* does," she muttered. "Look, just forget it. What I think doesn't mean anything, anyway. Go inside and get ready to make your speech. I'll stay here and greet those inevitable latecomers." She reached out and gave Anne a little push. "Go on."

She found herself standing beside the piano, saying the words she had said so many times that they came as second nature to her. It was a welcoming speech that always had a subtle bit of humor in it to make everyone relax. But though she knew it as well as she knew her own name, when she saw Karen usher Ross and her father into the room and seat them both in the back, her train of thought was very quickly derailed. She faltered and then stopped speaking. With that sudden start of surprise an audience that is only half-listening gives a speaker when they stop, every face in the room was turned toward her.

She forced herself to pick up where she had left off. "You'll be hearing many different levels of ability here tonight." Why did her voice suddenly sound low and throaty? Why were her knees shaking?

She chided herself inwardly and fought to concentrate on her words. "Please realize that for our students, their first appearance requires as much skill, courage, and control as that of a concert artist. Keep in mind that all the music you hear tonight, from the simplest Bach minuet to the most difficult concerto, represents hours of dedication and practice. We at the Runford Music School are justifiably proud of our students. We know you share that pride. Thank you for being here with them tonight."

She sat down to polite applause, dismayed to discover that as she opened her program her hands were shaking. That hadn't happened since the first recital she had hosted. She crossed her legs and tried to get comfortable in the straight-backed chair. She had to forget that Ross had intruded here in the small niche she had carved out for herself away from those heartbreaking memories of him. She had to forget that he was sitting there in the back row, his lithe body accomplishing the impossible task of looking at ease in the chair, his black hair glistening in the light of the overhead chandelier, his mouth lifted in that slight smile she remembered so well.

Somehow she did manage to direct her attention to the piano. One of her students, a little girl who had never played in public before, stumbled over a difficult part and recovered to go on and finish with a surge of self-confidence. She was pleased. She had tried to impress on the girl the importance of being able to recover from a mistake and go on. Evidently the girl had listened and remembered. Anne felt as much pride in her as she would have if the girl had played perfectly.

Dina was the last student to perform before the faculty quartet. She took her time getting ready, moving the bench back slightly, checking the position of her hands on the keyboard, and then moving the bench forward again. There was a nervous titter from one of the other students, but when Dina began to play, a breathless silence fell. The music soared out with power and control, infused with a depth of passion that seemed impossible for the young girl who sat at the piano to be achieving. Yet Anne knew that she had played with Dina's ability and skill at exactly the same tender age. . . .

Dina's performance was superb and earned her a long round of applause. She rose from the piano and inclined her dark head, glossy braids falling over her shoulders. Something about the girl as she stood there humbly acknowledging the applause she richly deserved made Anne ache to put her arms around her and hug her. Dina was young, vulnerable, and so very talented. Anne could only hope that her career in music would not be sidetracked as her own had been.

She was still thinking about Dina when the quartet walked to the front of the room, carrying their instruments and stands.

After they had seated themselves and checked their tuning one last time, they began to play.

They were all experienced artists who had studied music for several years. They put the audience at ease immediately with their confident playing.

At any other time, Anne would have given herself up to the enjoyment of the music. But tonight, for some reason, strange thoughts intruded. She sat staring at Michael, his fair hair falling over his forehead, his back bent lovingly over the cello, his long fingers stroking the fingerboard, his whole body absorbed in the act of playing. Jane, opposite him in the first violin position, was just as absorbed. She was a feminine echo of him.

What a strange thought to have.

The quartet played on. As if stimulated by the music, Anne's mind flashed images to her brain. She saw Shari sitting on the bed, mimicking Michael . . . Michael exchanging a dark look with Karen . . .

The music went on through the second and third movements to the end. In that instant before the applause began, Michael raised his head from his cello and looked across at Jane. Even in profile the euphoric, triumphant look she exchanged with him transformed her into a woman who was almost . . . beautiful. Then, as she got up to take her bow with the rest of the quartet, her eyes met Anne's. All her elation vanished, to be replaced by an emotion that contorted her face into harsh, bitter lines. The girl looked as if a prize she had thought hers had been taken away.

How stupid I've been, Anne thought with blinding clarity. *She loves him . . . and he is fighting what he feels for her—because of me. . . .*

She sat still and let her mind absorb the fact. She must have known it all along but refused to recognize it, until tonight, when the music forced her subconscious thoughts to meld with her conscious ones.

The ring on her finger didn't belong there. She would return it at once. Her fingertips touched the hard gold, felt the prongs that held the tiny stone in place. Her only regret was that she felt so little emotion.

"Anne." Her father, beaming, stood in front of her, extending his hand. She accepted it and allowed him to draw her to her feet. His eyes glistening, he said, "Dina plays like an angel. I was transported. You must be very proud."

"I am. Thank you, Father." She stood clutching his hand, trying to ignore the fact that Ross was standing politely to one side, a faint smile lifting his mouth as his eyes drifted over the grasp she maintained on the older man's hand. She flushed and pulled away.

"She reminds me of you at that age, you know," Owen Runford said, his face wistful.

"Yes," Ross said softly. "She does."

"Well, what a lovely family group." Michael's voice was intrusive, overly enthusiastic. Anne winced at his less-than-tactful linking of Ross with her father, and almost shrugged away the hand that came up to rest possessively on her shoulder. He said, "Did you enjoy the music, Mr. Runford?" and to Ross, "Mr. Leyton?"

"Very much indeed," Runford assured Michael. "The quartet has improved since I heard it last."

"We've been practicing some long hours." The hand on her shoulder lifted to her cheek. "What did you think of us, darling?"

Her eyes were caught by the sharp, suddenly dark look on Ross's face. She tried to concentrate on saying the words that Michael wanted to hear.

"Your ensemble playing was—excellent. Father's right about that. You've become a unit instead of four separate people playing together."

Michael's pleased smile lit his face. "Do you really think so?"

"Surely you must notice the difference. You all seem to be quite—attuned to one another."

He thrust his hand through his hair in an irritated gesture. "Bad joke."

Stung, she countered, "It wasn't a joke." A small flicker of pain darkened her eyes. She turned her head to search the recital hall for Dina, but as she did she caught sight of Ross's face. Quickly, before she could respond to that dark, empathetic look, she swung away and walked across the room.

At her approach, the family circle surrounding Dina opened slightly. She hugged the young girl and told her how proud she was. Tears of joy and pride shimmered in her eyes when she lifted her gaze over the girl's shoulder—to find Ross standing there. Watching. She gave Dina another quick hug and made her escape to the refreshment table.

"Who's the gorgeous male," Karen whispered as she took her place beside the girl and began to ladle the rosy drink into the fragile paper cups. "Is he here to sign up for lessons?" She rolled her eyes heavenward. "Don't I wish!"

"He's the new owner of Runford Glass." Anne's voice was dry.

Karen passed a paper plate across the table to the chubby, waiting hand of one of the little boys who had played cello. "Then maybe *I'll* take lessons—in glassblowing." She laughed, and Anne smiled.

She went on standing there behind the table, distributing cake and punch, each nerve in her body aware of him. When everyone had been served, there was nothing she could do but turn and say to him, "Would you care for something?"

His eyes gleamed. "Not right now. Are you—finished here?"

She tried to ignore Karen's interest in the conversation. But the girl had heard everything and said, "I'll stay here. You go ahead." Her dark eyes flashed with curiosity that Anne had no intention of satisfying.

Behind the table she was safe. Now she had to step out and let him take her elbow and pretend that it meant nothing to her to have those hard fingers on her bones. "What do you want?" Her voice was sharp, self-protective.

"Your father tells me you've been hoping to do some work on the rooms upstairs. Mind if I take a look?"

She wanted to say, yes, she minded a great deal, but the dark, slightly warning glint in his eye warned her not to.

"Yes, of course," she said coolly. "Help yourself. I'm sure you can find your way around. There are two stairways. The most convenient one is just off the entryway."

"I want you to come with me," he said, tightening his grip on her arm. "That way, I won't have to stumble around in the dark, trying to find light switches." Even as he said the words, he had propelled her through the crowd and out of the room and whatever choice she might have had in the matter evaporated.

The wooden stairs were broad enough for them to ascend side by side. The treads creaked alarmingly under their weight. Too late, she remembered how dismal the hallway looked with its broken patches of plaster and exposed lathe.

"Do the students use these stairs?" He frowned slightly.

"Yes. Both Michael's and Jane's studios are on the second floor."

She showed them to him, the big empty rooms that had little to recommend them except their high ceilings, wood floors, and huge windows that looked out over the town. In Michael's studio the only furniture was a scarred oak desk. Two straight-backed chairs faced music stands in front of it. A picture showing a child seated, playing the cello, hung on one wall.

"No pianos for accompaniment?" he asked, his head turning to look around the barren room.

"No. The second floor would have to be shored up with beams before the floor could support the weight of a piano. We had an architect give us an estimate of the cost, but—"

"You don't have the money."

She turned to face him. "That should be obvious, to you, of all people."

"Have you thought about using a portable Rhodes electric piano? It couldn't weigh any more than that monster of a desk, and you could move it from room to room as you needed it."

She stared at him. "I—I hadn't thought about using an electric piano."

The corners of his lips curved. "Too modern for a classicist like you?"

"No, of course not. It wouldn't matter that much just for rehearsal." She twisted away, wanting to get him out of her vision. His instant, creative solution to a problem they had thought insoluble disturbed her. She had forgotten how quick and incisive his mind was. No wonder he was a successful executive.

"Do you have a studio?" He went out of the room, but instead of turning back to the front stairs, he walked toward the narrow back stairway. She followed, turning off lights as she went. "No. I teach on the grand piano downstairs."

They were in the kitchen now, and she watched as his eyes flickered over the archaic hand pump that stood beside the sink. "You must have an office of some kind."

"Yes—I do." Alarmed, she made an attempt to lead him into the main rooms. He caught her back. "Is that it through that door there?"

She nodded, her throat full. Something hard and painful twisted inside her. He was leaving her no sanctuary, no space that he had not invaded with his presence.

Silently he moved to the door and pulled it open. A soft sound of protest escaped her throat, and she followed him, praying that he would merely look around and then walk out. He didn't. He stood with his back to her, but from the angle of his dark head, she knew he was examining the carpeted walls and ceiling. When he swung around to face her, something in his expression made her say, "This can't be of any interest to you."

"Everything about you interests me," he said softly. While she was grappling with the connotations of that, he reached around

94

her and pushed the door shut. She was trapped with him in the soundproof room.

Trembling with anger, she stood her ground. He hesitated, as if something in her face warned him of her barely leashed temper. Then, as if he had assessed the dangers and decided on a plan of action, he caught hold of her upper arms and hauled her close to him. "Why? Why are you hiding away in your home town in this padded cell—when ten years ago you were headed for a career as a concert artist?"

"That's not true—" She struggled, wanting desperately to get away from him.

"It is," he contradicted her coldly. "You had been studying with a master teacher for years. He had already suggested you request a date at Carnegie Hall."

She straightened her back and met his eyes, a liquid emerald fire in hers. She wanted to scream at him, "*you, Ross Leyton. You are the reason*" . . . but she couldn't. She couldn't give him the satisfaction of knowing just how destroyed she had been by his rejection.

"What I did or didn't do with my life is my business, not yours." Her voice was icy with disdain. "Let go of me."

"No." He had her trapped between the door and his hard length. "No . . ." Instead of holding her against the door for the kiss she knew he meant to punish her with, he lifted her away and cradled her in his hands, one at the nape of her neck, and the other at the low, sensitive spot on her back. The soft black wool dress she wore was no protection from the burning weight of his fingers.

An instant before his mouth covered hers, she said wildly, "Ross—don't." She groped for the words that would stop that inevitable path of his mouth toward hers. She couldn't let him kiss her again. "I'm—wearing another man's ring. I belong to him. . . ."

He paused for a fraction of a second, as if he were considering it. Then something hard and determined flashed in his eyes, and his mouth moved lower, but he didn't really kiss her. He talked to her, his mouth moving provocatively over hers, his warm breath fanning her mouth. "He's not right for you, Anne. He doesn't begin to understand the lovely complexity of you. You wouldn't last two weeks with him."

His lips rested lightly on hers, tantalizing her, like the brush of a hummingbird's vibrating wing. That touch of his mouth was somehow more wildly exciting, more sensually intimate, than a hard kiss would have been. He was just simply—there—on her mouth, and he wasn't going away. She moved restlessly, and felt the light flick of his tongue against her lip. "Ross—" With a quick swoop, he was inside, tasting the honey sweetness of her. A soft moan escaped her throat, and memory and sensation mingled to send aching need tingling to the bottom of her spine. Cold reason screamed a warning in her brain, but she ignored it and let Ross discover the contours of her mouth as he had that first morning when he kissed her in the cool, crisp dawn so long ago. The hands that should have pushed him away went around his neck to keep him close, his mouth locked tightly against hers. She clung to him, shamelessly molding her body to his.

After a long, breathless time, he raised his head. His eyes glittered over her, a satisfied gleam in their depths. He looked like a sleek male tiger who had just feasted on a tasty meal. "Now," he said. "Tell me that you belong to another man."

His challenge brought her out of her sensual haze. She put her palms against his chest and gave him a vicious shove. "Get away from me."

Just an instant after she stopped pushing, he stepped back, showing her that it was his decision that parted them. His hands fell away from her shoulders. "I'm away," he said softly, watching her.

Perversely she felt cold and deserted—and extremely annoyed. A slight smile tipped the corners of his mouth as he watched those conflicting emotions play across her face. Her temper soared. "Don't you ever kiss me like that again."

"My dear Anne." His smile broadened. "You wound me to the bottom of my creative heart. Of course I won't kiss you like that again. I'll think of something entirely different the next time."

Boldly he stepped forward and brushed a kiss on her ear. Then, before she could move, he walked calmly around her and pulled open the door. She whirled around, seething with an angry violence to do him injury. Casually, his hand resting on the doorknob, he turned. "Oh, by the way. After we sign that contract, I'll have an electric piano delivered to the school."

Her eyes darkened, but before she could say anything he gave her a mocking nod of his dark head and went out the door, closing it behind him.

"Oh—oh—" She breathed in sharply and backed up against the desk. Her fingers closed over the glass paperweight and in one swift motion, she raised her arm and sent it flying. The heavy paperweight hit the door with a resounding crack—and shattered into a million pieces.

Her protective cocoon was gone. All of it. Ross had come back, and she was as vulnerable to him as she had been at seventeen.

It was the quiet that brought her to her senses. She wrenched open the door and fled from the room. The recital hall was empty—and dark. Karen must have turned out the lights and locked the door, believing that she was gone. The room was dark, except for the moonlight that gleamed on the raised lid of the grand piano and slid down to pool on the keys.

As if drawn by an invisible force, she moved toward it—and sat down. Her hands hovered above it for a breathless second. Then the heavy, dark chords of the Brahms *Rhapsody* soared out into the silence. She was playing, playing with a brilliance and power she hadn't allowed herself to express in years.

The cadences of the music rose and fell. She played on, knowing that her playing was flawless, knowing that in this dark room, alone, she was creating a thing of beauty that would live on forever—if only in her mind.

Then it was over, and she dropped her hands in her lap. Utterly spent, she sat like a statue in the moonlight.

"Anne."

She should have sensed he was there. Perhaps in a way, she had.

"That was magnificient." Ross moved away from the entryway, a tall, masculine shadow in a room full of shadows.

She stood up, too drained by the gamut of emotions she had run to think of anything but leaving. "I'm going home."

It was too dark to see the expression on his face. "I'll follow you in my car to see that you arrive safely."

CHAPTER SIX

The next morning Anne drove to the school, unlocked the door, and went directly to the kitchen. She would need something to put the shattered pieces of glass paperweight in. After hunting through several cupboards, she found a tin can that would suffice. Unlocking her office door, she was relieved to see that the sunlight streaming through the kitchen window glittered off the shards, making them easy to see. She knelt and began to pick them up, using extreme caution. They made a tiny clinking noise as she deposited them in the can.

Her loose hair fell over her cheek and the sun's rays turned it to the color of spun gold. She thrust it back with an impatient hand and went on with her task.

The outer door opened and closed, and Karen's heels clicked along the recital hall floor and rounded the corner. "Good lord. I nearly fell over you!" The clicking heels moved around her. "What are you doing?"

"Picking up broken glass." Anne rocked back on her haunches and had the distinct feeling she was stating the obvious.

"Did we have vandals last night?" Anne could hear the worried tone in Karen's voice. "I was sure I locked everything, and

I didn't notice anything wrong with the door when I came in this morning—"

"There were no vandals."

"Well, something certainly must have struck. There are even bits of glass in the carpeting on the wall." She stepped to one side of Anne and plucked a glittering chip from a strand of the yellow shag carpeting. Following Anne's example, she dropped it in the can. "What is—or was—this thing we're picking up in eight million pieces?"

"It's my paperweight."

Karen was instantly sympathetic. "Oh, Anne, not your favorite, the one you loved so much. I'm so sorry. How did it happen?"

"I threw it at the door." There was something therapeutic about admitting she had committed the act of violence.

"You—threw it at the door?" Karen had knelt to help Anne, but now she rocked back on her heels and stared at the other girl. "Why?" Then comprehension and relief flared in her eyes. "Oh, you found out about—" Her eyes searched downward for Anne's ring finger, and when she saw the ring, she swallowed and said, "Oh—" and closed her mouth abruptly.

Anne lifted cool green eyes to the girl. Michael's involvement with Jane must have gone deeper than exchanged glances if Karen knew about it. How many others were aware that her engagement was a farce? "Did I find out about what?" She met Karen's eyes steadily.

Karen couldn't hold the gaze. Her eyes skittered away, and she made a pretense of examining the rug for more glass. "I just thought maybe you found out about the—that you were going to have to close the school." She hesitated, and Anne gave her full marks for a valiant effort at protecting Anne's feelings. "Everybody's been wondering," she finished off, a trifle lamely.

"The school isn't going to close." She bent her head and went on picking up the particles. "The Leyton conglomerate has agreed to continue financing us."

Karen expelled a short breath. "I'm glad." She gave Anne a wry glance. "I wasn't looking forward to the idea of going through the job-hunting scene all over again."

"Well, you won't have to. You have your job here for as long as you want it. Everyone does," she added swiftly. She lifted her head to search for more flecks of glass, very aware of Karen's eyes on her. There was a curious, almost apprehensive look on the girl's face. Was Karen thinking of Michael and wondering if he would be secure in his position if Anne discovered that he was involved with Jane? Inwardly she shuddered. That was another problem she had to resolve—and quickly, before she left Runford on the planned trip to see her mother.

She picked up the container of broken glass and straightened. "Has Michael come in yet?"

Karen started. "Oh, my gosh. I forgot all about the reason I came to see you. His student is here—but he isn't. I wondered if you wanted to call him."

"Michael never oversleeps," Anne said. *Let her think about that one!* She walked around the girl and went into the kitchen with her burden, hiding a smile at the slightly dazed look Karen was wearing. "I suppose he's got car trouble again." She raised her voice so that Karen could hear her as she bent to deposit the container in the trash. "I'd better go pick him up. He's probably walking somewhere between here and school."

"Probably," Karen said, following her into the kitchen. "All I know is that if his ten o'clock students come a few more times when he isn't here, they're going to stop coming on time, or else stop coming altogether."

"You're right," Anne replied. "I'll mention that to him."

She drove down Farragut and left on Elm, the sun bright in her eyes, the snow crunching under the tires. Though her car was moving slowly and she was watching carefully for him, Anne saw no sign of Michael. She thought about the possibility that he might have gone another way—and discarded it. Knowing he was already late, he would have taken the most direct route. Where was he?

She continued to drive down the street toward his home and arrived in front of the house that had been subdivided to contain his large ground-floor apartment. A little butterfly began to beat against the pit of her stomach. Jane's car sat at the curb.

She turned off the engine. She supposed the discreet thing to do would be to turn around and go back to the school and call him. But something, some need to know the truth about herself as well as Michael, forced her to open the door of the car and step down onto the sidewalk.

The cold air closed around her, squeezing the breath from her lungs. Her booted feet sounded unnaturally loud as she walked across the wooden floor. She raised a gloved hand to the doorbell —and her courage failed her. She turned to go, but it was too late to make an escape. Her footsteps had been heard. Muffled voices and scuffling sounds came from inside.

Caught, there was nothing she could do but press the small white button with the name Adams above it.

At the sound of the buzzer there was more noise from within, more hushed conversation. Then it became unnaturally quiet and a long moment went by. If she could have walked across the porch and got into her car without being seen, she would have. But she couldn't.

The inside door swung open, and an astonished Michael, his fair hair tousled, his brown robe slightly baring one shoulder, as if he had thrown it on very quickly, appeared in the doorway. His feet were bare. In that instant, seeing him off guard, vulnerable, Anne felt a fleeting stab of regret, which was immediately followed by the cool thought that she had loved him in the same way she loved Dina. They had shared a love of music—and little else.

At the sight of her on his doorstep he paled. "Anne." There was a choked quality in the way he said her name.

"Hello, Michael." She wanted to make this as easy for both

102

of them as she possibly could. The memory of her own reaction to Ross's kiss made her say softly, "I—I need to talk to you. May I come in? It's rather cold out here, and you're going to catch your death standing there with just your robe on."

His hand slid down the side of his thigh, and there was a look of surprise on his face, as if he had forgotten what he was wearing. His hesitation was only momentary. "Yes, of course, come in."

She stepped inside, and he closed the door behind her. The apartment looked just as it always had, bare of furniture except for the easy chair and a card table that Michael used for his sporadic composing. The stereo cabinet door was open, and a record jacket of a John Cage album was propped against it. The bedroom door was tightly closed.

A long-fingered hand came up to worry through his hair. "Is—anything wrong?"

"No . . ." she said carefully, "only that you have a pupil waiting for you."

"Oh, blast. The confounded alarm must not have gone off. I suppose Richard's waiting for me." His fingers went to the belt of his robe as he restlessly tightened the knot.

"He was a few minutes ago. How much longer he'll wait, I don't know." She tugged at her gloves. "Will you need a ride back to the school—" She hesitated, not really wanting to say what she had planned to say. But a sixth sense told her that if she didn't press him to admit that he and Jane were lovers, he might try to convince her later that it had all been her imagination. And worse, she might allow him to do it, and go on wearing his ring and hiding behind a meaningless engagement in order to avoid facing the fact that she had never got over her life-long obsession for Ross. "Or"—she took a breath—"were you going to go back with Jane?"

"Jane?" His light eyebrows flew up. He was silent for a moment, fighting valiantly to regain his poise. "I don't know what you're talking about."

"Her car is outside." Her voice was soft, almost gentle, as if she were speaking to a child.

"Oh, that." He made a grimace. "Well, you see, she stopped by last night after the recital, and we were both on such a high that I suggested we listen to some music. Then we had some coffee, but when she went out to start her car—it wouldn't start. So she left it here and walked home—"

"Michael, you don't have to say any more. I understand."

There was a harsh sound, an intake of breath. Beyond Michael's shoulder, Jane stood framed in the doorway of the bedroom. She had on a short toweling robe, and with her hair down and her face flushed with a curious combination of embarrassment and pride, she was almost as beautiful as she had been last night. "Don't lie to her anymore, Michael."

Michael turned, saw her, and said a short, harsh word.

"Hello, Jane," Anne said calmly.

"You knew I was here." Jane's voice was low and trembling with restrained emotion as she met Anne's gaze steadily.

"Yes." She held out the ring to Michael.

"Oh, God, Anne, listen to me. This thing between Jane and me just happened one night after rehearsal, and then—there didn't seem to be any way to stop it—or to tell you—"

She pressed the ring into his hand. He took it reluctantly and then tried to catch her fingers, but she drew them away. The blood that had left his face earlier when he discovered her at his door rushed into his cheeks. "I was—always—fond of you, Anne."

"But that's not enough, is it," she murmured.

His chin high, he said, "You'll have my resignation by noon—"

"I don't want your resignation," she told him bluntly. "Ross has agreed to fund the school. Does that meet with your approval?"

He seemed stunned. "Of course, but—"

"The school is in the strongest position financially it has been

104

in years with backing from Western Data. We'll need a youthful, enthusiastic director like you to attract both new faculty and new students if we're to experience the growth my father and I have always dreamed of." She gave him a clear, direct look. "You're an accomplished musician and you teach well. Your job is secure for whatever length of time you want it."

His shoulders sagged with relief. "You don't know what this means to me—"

She glanced beyond him at the tense girl whose eyes had never left him.

"I hope it will mean something for both of you," she said and turned abruptly to leave them.

"What time did you say he was coming?" Shari asked Anne for the tenth time. "Oh, my hair looks simply awful."

Shari was staring at herself in her dresser mirror, her face wreathed in exasperation, when Anne walked into the room. Anne's eyes played over the girl's mirror image, which, contrary to Shari's words, looked lovely. The young girl wore a silk ice-blue dress that hung from tiny straps and bloused out over her high breasts to be caught in at her narrow waist with a silver belt. A flaring skirt rustled over sleek nylon-clad legs.

"He'll be here in fifteen minutes," Anne said calmly. "Is there anything I can do to help?"

"Yes," Shari said, giving her sister a mock-murderous glance. "You can go back to your room and take off that sexy red dress that shows all your shoulders—where did you get it, anyway—and you can put your hair back up into that dreadful bun you usually wear it in instead of letting it drift over your back, and you can go break your leg so Ross and I can be alone."

Anne rolled her eyes heavenward and advanced into the room. Shari's litany went on unabated. "How do you expect Ross to even notice me when you walk around looking like a combination of Cheryl Tiegs and Greta Garbo?"

"Greta Garbo? What do you know about Greta Garbo?"

"I know she was mysterious and sexy and told everybody she wanted to be alone. And that's the way you are. There's an air of mystery about you, as if you have a secret that you're never going to tell. You look so, . . . intriguing." She sighed. "How can I compete with that?"

Anne bit back a sharp comment. She couldn't add to Ross's already strong attraction by making him forbidden fruit. "You'll have to do the opposite thing and scintillate," she chided the girl lightly.

Shari made a face in the mirror. "How can I do something I can't even pronounce?" Her mouth set in tense concentration, she drew a narrow line of eyeliner just above her lashes. "Why couldn't I have had your blond hair instead of this stuff that curls no matter what I do?"

"Lots of girls would give anything to have your dark curls," she said.

"Lots of girls can have it—free of charge. I'll cut it off and give it to them." She grabbed a lock and pulled it out from the side of her head to let it go and watch it spring back to its former curl. "I can't do anything *different* with it. It always looks the same." She shot a swift, wicked look at Anne. "Maybe when I get to Mother's, I can ask her what she does with hers."

"At least it will give you a topic of conversation," she said crisply, all too aware that she hadn't succeeded in keeping the arid bite out of her tone as she should have.

Shari twisted around on the bench. "You really do have a thing about Mother, don't you."

"Why don't you finish your makeup? We don't have time to launch into a serious discussion of my hang-ups. It would take too long." She smiled and put her hands on Shari's shoulders to turn her around on the bench.

Shari allowed herself to be turned, but her eyes were bright in the light of the lamps, her gaze focused on the hands Anne let linger on her shoulders. "You've forgotten to put your ring on."

Their eyes met in the glassy reflection. "No, I haven't," she said evenly.

"You mean you're not going to wear it tonight?" Shari persisted.

"Not tonight—or any other night."

"You've given it back?" Shari's eyes sparkled with curiosity. "When? When did all this happen? Why didn't you tell me?"

The questions scattered over her. "This morning, actually." She broke off Shari's probing eye contact and said, "I really think you should finish getting ready—"

Totally disregarding the advice, Shari countered, "And you didn't breathe a word to me." She picked up the eyeliner, a barely controlled excitement bubbling in her voice. "See what I mean about looking as if you had a secret? You did, didn't you?"

"Well, it certainly won't be a secret for long."

Shari's hand moved carefully along the bottom of her other eye. "What are you going to do—now?"

"What do you mean . . . do?"

"Well you aren't going to go on teaching at the school, are you—I mean, with Michael there and all. . . ."

"Of course I am. Why shouldn't I?"

"Won't it be embarrassing?"

"I'm sure there will be an adjustment period for everyone. But our—involvement will soon be forgotten. Life goes on, honey."

Shari finished and rose from the bench with a swish of chiffon and silk. "See?" There was a touch of triumph in her voice. "I told you he wasn't for you. I was right, wasn't I?"

"It seems you were," Anne murmured.

"What happened to make you break it off?"

The sound of the doorbell chimed through the house. Even the arrival of Ross Leyton was preferable to fending off an attack of questions launched by her sister.

When they had got into their coats and were leaving the house, with Ross's hand guiding them over the icy path, Anne was thankful for Shari's vivacious chatter. Ross had been formally polite at the door, but his gray eyes were far too keen. Inside the car, seated away from him on the other side of Shari, she was glad to be away from them. Was he remembering how she had played last night while he stood listening? Had he heard the passion flare to life—passion that she hadn't released since the day she had lain in his arms?

The Inn was brightly lit, an island of warmth throwing squares of light on the snow. Green plants the size of small trees thrived in a glass entryway, looking as if they had sprung up around an oasis in the bleak winter terrain.

Ross parked the car close, and Anne climbed out before he could come around to help her, but Shari smiled and extended her hand as if she were granting him a favor. Where had she learned those feminine wiles? At her age, Anne had been a gauche teenager who knew nothing of men.

But she had learned. Dear God, she had learned. And the man beside her, striding up the steps with the lithe ease of an athlete, had been her teacher. . . . How she hated him for betraying her!

In contrast her reaction to giving Michael back his ring had been almost negligent, except that, that afternoon, a wild, unreasoning urge to look stunning had driven her to make an impromptu shopping trip that had resulted in the purchase of the red dress she wore. But now, here beside Ross, handing over her coat to the elderly woman who was putting her book down to take it, she regretted her impulsiveness. In the store, she had thought that the way the fitted red sheath with its strapless bodice clung to her breasts and outlined her hips was what she needed to bolster her confidence to endure this evening. But it was only as she turned to walk ahead of Ross into the dining room that she realized that the gown was designed so that she had to swivel her hips slightly from side to side in order to move.

One part of her mind revolted, but the other, sensuous side of her, unleashed last night, found a perverse enjoyment in knowing that she looked like an attractive, desirable woman, and that men were looking at her as she walked toward the table.

If the men were looking at her, the women were certainly finding the sight of Ross riveting. She could imagine what an effect he was making as he strode along behind her in his camel suit of finest cashmere, a soft off-white shirt lying against his skin, the sensuous luxury of his clothes somehow accenting the sheer maleness of him.

They were seated a few tables away from the spot where she had sat with Michael only a few nights ago. Had it been so recent? It seemed an eternity. And perhaps it was. She had lived a lifetime since she had played the *Rhapsody* in the darkened recital hall.

Ross seated Shari on the window side of the table and sat down next to her, directly across from Anne.

"Umm, what a super view." Shari's head was turned as she gazed out at the dark countryside covered with snow. "This is perfect."

"Yes," Ross murmured, his eyes fastened on Anne. "Isn't it?" His eyes moved slowly over the creamy perfection of her shoulders down to that tantalizing glimpse of soft curves above the line of red material.

The menus were large and silver, and she picked one up and held it in front of her casually, as if she were not purposely shielding her upper body from Ross's view.

"Have you decided what you'd like?" The low tone seemed to be asking a much more intimate question than her choice of food.

She raised her eyes and gave him a long, cool look. "I think I'll have the sole." She tossed the words at him, their edges sharp with double meaning. Ross had given her his body but he had never given her his soul. "It's so rarely offered. . . ."

He knew exactly what she meant. Twin flames of anger burned in his dark eyes. Then he cooled his anger and a quirking smile flickered over his mouth. "And what would you recommend for me? A large order of crow?" His voice was soft with a note of self-mockery that nearly made her smile.

Shari exclaimed, "Fish! Ugh. I don't want fish. I'll have the steak and lobster." She had missed their low exchange entirely.

"Surf and turf? Yes, that does sound good," Ross said easily, his tone a sharp contrast to the anger that had burned in his eyes a moment ago.

A young man took their order for wine and a soft drink for Shari. When he was gone, the girl turned to Ross. "Please, can't I have just a taste?"

He gave her another lazy smile. "Sometimes a taste can be just as dangerous as a full measure. Better wait, little one."

A bittersweet regret washed over Anne. If only she hadn't been so impatient to taste the fruits of love. It was a restless prodding thought, one that urged her to say crisply, "The contract will be ready for you Monday afternoon. Will you be available?"

"Yes." He gave her an appraising glance.

"Shall we say, two o'clock, then? At my father's office?"

"Two is fine." A lifted eyebrow mocked her business-crisp tone.

Shari frowned and shot Anne a puzzled look. "What's this about a contract?"

As if Ross had asked the words out loud, they shone in his eyes. *Do you want her to know?*

A quick shake of her head told him she didn't. Ross turned to Shari and gave her the full force of his warm smile. "Just some business your sister and I have to complete—and it isn't any of yours." He brought his hand up to punctuate his words by brushing his fingertip carelessly down Shari's nose.

Under the combined influence of his potent charm and physical touch, Shari melted. "What about our trip?" she asked, her eyes adoring him. "When are we going to see our mother?"

"We'll talk about that after we've eaten," he said firmly, and Shari subsided back into her chair.

Anne shifted slightly and fought the urge to lift her silver sandal and place a well-aimed kick just above Ross's polished

shoes. Ross could have told Shari to walk over hot coals and she would have. It was dangerous, this burgeoning crush she was developing, couldn't Ross see that? Was there anything she could do to stop it? She doubted it. But did she need to, really? That experienced mouth, those hands with their covering of dark hair and neatly trimmed nails, that hard man's body, had taken pleasure from women who were experts in the art of love. He certainly wouldn't think of amusing himself with a young girl.
. . .

He did once, her mind whispered, and the hand that was clenched under the table turned into a curving claw that punished her own skin.

She was only too willing to accept the wineglass that the steward offered a moment later. But when she reached for it, a new, more dangerous complication presented itself. Ross's eyes fastened on the hand that was lifting the glass to her lips, the finger that no longer wore Michael's ring. His pupils flared, as if he had suffered a shock. Then, before she could begin to fathom the thoughts that lay behind those gray depths, he dropped his lashes, barring her from seeing whatever there might have been to see.

What did she expect to see? Mild curiosity, perhaps. Surely nothing more—because he cared nothing for her. He had proved that. He might, under the influence of Shari's prolonged adoration, consent to play the part of a protective older brother for as long as it amused him, but never, in a million years, could she accept him in that role. It was true, he had once been her friend . . . until he became her lover. Now he was neither.

Their meal seemed slow in coming. Shari and Ross's amiable chatting gave her a feeling of edgy irritability. How did he happen to know so much about high school history, chemistry, basketball? He even commiserated with her about not getting a part in the play the Drama Club was producing in March.

"It's just as well," he told her. "You would have missed the rehearsals while you're away."

"That's true." Shari brightened and flashed a smile at him. "I hadn't thought of that."

After what seemed an interminable length of time, the food was brought to their table on heavy stainless steel trays. It was the diversion she needed to help her whip her errant mind into submission.

She couldn't have said afterward what she ate or what they talked about. All her sensory receptors seemed to be tuned toward the man who sat across the table from her. She was overwhelmingly conscious of the aura of tension that seemed to emanate from Ross whenever their eyes met. It was as if he were waiting, waiting with a barely concealed impatience that made the air crackle around her.

Unnerved, she drank too much and ate too little. Shari said something, and Anne heard her own laughter bubble from her throat. She was amazed. What did she have to laugh about?

The Inn featured live music on Saturday night, and just after their dishes were taken away and they requested coffee, the musicians began to play. The music was soft, allowing low conversation to continue. Across the room from them, between the dining room and the bar area, a small square of wooden floor had been cleared for dancing.

Shari glanced at Ross, her face expectant. He took his cue and said, "Would you like to dance?"

"Yes," she answered without any hesitation, and gazed at him as he stood to help her out of her chair.

Other than Ross's polite "Excuse us, won't you," neither of them seemed to give Anne a second thought. She watched them move out on the dance floor, and when Shari turned into Ross's arms, a hard knot twisted inside her. Ross's hand against the blue chiffon at the back of Shari's waist looked tanned and male and utterly—possessive. Her young face was lifted toward his, and he smiled down at her and held her carefully, as if he had been entrusted with a fragile treasure.

They might have been brother and sister with their dark hair.

They were alike, too, in their air of assurance. Other than the occasional complaint about her hair, Shari had never suffered the pangs of insecurity that had plagued Anne. But, of course, Shari's girlhood was normal, filled with parties and telephone calls. Anne had seen to that. She had decided long ago that Shari would not spend two thirds of her life at the piano, away from the normal social exchanges of young people.

Stop it! You're envious of your sister—not because she had a normal upbringing, but because she is dancing with Ross. You're jealous of anyone who touches him. And you have no right.
. . .

Her face burned. How could she be thinking these things about her sister? She loved Shari. She had nursed her through chicken pox and scraped knees, and the pangs of first love. Together they had forged a relationship that somehow walked a thin line between sisters and guardian. She couldn't let this—obsession she had for Ross damage that relationship.

She looked up and saw them then, walking back from the dance floor. Shari, with Ross's arm on her elbow, was flushed and beaming.

"That was marvelous. Thank you." Shari smiled her appreciation for the dance at him as he seated her. He answered her smile, his lips curved.

The hands that had been trained to respond to every nuance of Anne's intellect and emotion were clenched. Fingernails bit into her palms. The ache in the pit of her stomach seemed to be permanently lodged there. Oh, God, this had to stop. She would control her feelings, she must.

A white-coated waiter brought their coffee in tall brown mugs and set them in front of them, completing his task by placing a large pitcher of cream in the middle of the table. Ross eyed it, a smile twitching his lips. "I haven't seen real cream in years. I had forgotten we were in the middle of dairy country."

Shari made a face. "Don't remind me."

He turned slightly to give her a tolerant look. "Nowadays the

113

person who can make a living on the farm is considered fortunate."

The well-shaped nose wrinkled. "They can have it." She sat quietly for a moment and then said, "Where does Mother live, Ross?"

He gave the pitcher a quick tip over his mug and picked up his spoon. "Right now she's in Florida."

Shari sat up straighter. "Florida! I thought we'd be going to California."

"Did you?" His gaze on her was speculative. "The conglomerate is based in California, but my father and Leora have lived in Florida for the last five years."

A wash of conflicting emotions swirled around inside Anne. She had thought a visit to her mother would mean prolonged exposure to Ross. Discovering it didn't should have brought exquisite relief . . . not this sharp disappointment. "Where in Florida? Miami?"

He swung his head away from Shari and studied her. "No, not Miami. They have a place out of the mainstream, away from publicity."

Shari leaned forward. "You make it sound so mysterious."

Ross sipped his coffee and then set the mug on the table. "Am I? I'm not trying to. I'm merely saying that not many people know where they are—and they wish it to remain that way."

"Aren't you going to tell us?" Shari's face was animated with the thought of sharing a secret.

Ross was thoughtful for a moment. Then he said, "No, I'd prefer not to."

Pink color stained Anne's cheeks. "You don't trust us not to reveal the whereabouts of this—mysterious retreat?"

His eyes never left hers. "It isn't a matter of trust. It's a protective measure." His gaze moved slowly over her face and came to rest on her mouth. "You must admit that because of my father's position and the—circumstances of his marriage to your mother, your visit—would be newsworthy. If anyone from the

114

press got curious, we'd have reporters staked out at the house on a twenty-four-hour watch. And I don't want that. I want your visit to be a pleasant one."

Anne's mouth twisted. "That's being very optimistic."

The tension she had felt seemed to increase palpably, radiating from Ross in waves. But he kept a firm guard on his answer. "No," he said in a deceivingly bland tone, "I don't think it is. My father and Leora are looking forward to your coming with great anticipation. I'm sure you wouldn't want to be an ingracious guest."

His words were cool, but the gray eyes were not. They flashed a warning as clearly as if he had said it. *Don't involve Shari in this.*

She averted her eyes. She owed him that, she supposed. And she owed that to Shari, too. Shari had a right to make her own decisions about her mother without feelings of misguided loyalty to Anne.

"You're right, of course." Her voice was husky. Not wanting to look at Ross, she stared at the flickering flame of the candle. Why, of all the people involved, was she the one who found it so hard to forgive her mother?

Because you needed her desperately back then, the answer came back. *You were on the verge of falling apart, physically, mentally, emotionally. Your pride, your self-respect, your belief in the deep love of one human being for another had been ground in the dust . . . no, drowned in the river,* she thought with a rueful twist of her mouth.

If only she hadn't known him so well, she thought desperately. If it had been only a casual sexual encounter, she could have understood his unfeeling use of her. But she had known him for years. Over and over again she had asked herself why. Why had he made love to her and talked of marriage—knowing he was never going to marry her? She had never known him to be less than truthful in even the smallest things. Yet in the most important thing of all, he had practiced a deception of the cruelest kind.

Some invisible force drew her eyes away from the candle up to his face. Reflected in the candlelight, those eyes that had been almost black with anger a moment ago burned with a dark, complex mixture of emotions she couldn't read. Pain might have been one—regret another. She couldn't look away. It was as if for the first time she was seeing into his soul, because he wanted her to. And she knew she wasn't misreading his agony. It wasn't only his eyes that were tormented, it was his mouth, too. His lips were held in an unrelenting line, and his jaw was tight, as if he were clenching his teeth to keep the words that burned in his brain from tumbling out.

The candle flickered crazily, and a mask seemed to slip down over his face. In that instant his eyes cooled, his mouth relaxed. She tore her gaze from his face, sure that she had imagined everything.

"Dance with me." The low invitation startled her. She opened her mouth to refuse and then lifted her head. In another few hours this evening would be over, and he would fly back to California. She would never see him again. She would be safe. What harm could possibly come from moving around a crowded dance floor in his arms for a few minutes?

"All right." She rose from her chair and walked ahead of him. If he was surprised at her quick acceptance, she saw no sign of it.

She turned and lifted her arm. He clasped her cool fingers in his warm ones. The pressure of his fingers on her back was light, but controlling. Tensely she waited for him to pull her close. But he didn't. She was just barely in his arms, held carefully, a space between them, almost as if they were students at a dancing school.

He circled around with her, and an unreasoning anger grew stronger with every step. How could he hold her like this when

116

he had drawn Shari so close and held her with such evident pleasure?

Her anger needed a vent. "How very circumspect you are suddenly," she mocked lightly.

He looked at her in feigned surprise. "In what way?"

There was a knowing undertone in his voice that told her he knew exactly what she was talking about. "Nothing, it doesn't matter." Why did she have this absurd urge to burst into tears?

"Is there something wrong?" The words were incisive.

Her defenses down, she murmured the truth. "Yes, everything's wrong. My being in your arms is wrong—"

His hands tightened. She tried to fend him off, but he pulled her to him with a gruff, impatient sound. The soft cloth of his suit brushed her bare shoulders, the hard muscles of his thighs and legs pressed intimately against hers. His masculine scent, a mixture of tangy soap and cologne that was particularly his, filled her nose.

Too late, she saw the trap. He had held her away intentionally, knowing exactly how she would react, knowing that once she had been denied his closeness, she would crave it like a drug—and accept it willingly when it was offered.

But she was accepting it. She made no move to push herself away. She couldn't. Deep inside, a molten core seemed to melt and expand. His chest against her breasts gave erotic pleasure, his mouth breathed magic into her hair. Her senses were immersed in him, her skin absorbing him through her pores. An intolerable ache radiated upward through her.

The music stopped. Abruptly he released her. A chill shivered over her skin as she walked back to the table. What a fool she was to think she could dance with him without harm! She had glimpsed heaven, and having seen it, resented its loss all the more.

She sat down in the chair and longed for the freedom to go home, to go to her room and bury her head in the pillow and beat her fists on the bed. For ten long years she had whipped her feelings for Ross into submission—and had even succeeded to the point where she could risk getting engaged to another man. Now, in just three days, she had been flung back into that dark abyss she remembered so well, back to those anguished days and nights that followed Ross's betrayal.

"Umm, they're playing a disco song. Will you dance with me again, Ross—please?" Shari's voice seemed to be coming from another planet.

"What makes you think an old fogy like me knows how to disco?" Ross's tone was indulgent, amused. Anne wrapped her hands around the coffee mug that had been filled in her absence. Her cold fingers seemed to be immune to the heat.

Shari's eyes flashed. "You're not an old fogy. And I'll bet you do know how to disco, don't you?"

He rose, smiling. "Maybe you can teach me some new steps."

Anne sipped her coffee, averting her eyes from Ross and Shari as they walked away. But inevitably her gaze fastened on the dark-haired couple moving easily on the dance floor. Shari's blue dress moved sensuously around her legs as she stood opposite Ross and bent and swayed. They were mirror images, Shari dancing with all the exuberance of her age, Ross moving with an ease that was fluid and controlled—and very male. His jacket slid over his lean hips as he circled, and his lips were lifted in a smile that encouraged Shari to execute ever newer, more daring steps.

She endured the exquisite torture of watching them for as long as she could and then turned her head to look out the window at the snowy countryside.

The music ended. "Please, Ross. Just one more dance." Shari was following him to the table, tugging on his arm.

"It's time you were in bed, young lady." He laid a large bill on the check and said to Anne, "I'll take you home now."

It was a relief to allow him to help her on with her coat, even though his fingers brushed her bare shoulders and burned where

118

they touched. Outside, the wind had risen, and the night air was biting, astringent against her lips, like a sip of sharp wine.

This time she let him help her into the car. In a matter of seconds, it seemed, they were out of the parking lot and on the snow-covered road. As if she were in a state of limbo, she watched the countryside flash by. Ross drove at a rate of speed that betrayed his eagerness for the evening to end. Even Shari lapsed into quietness. Anne took a deep breath and pressed her forehead against the glass of the car window. Her ordeal was over. She would never see him again.

The unnatural quiet lasted until they reached the house and got out of the car.

"Give me your key," Ross said to Shari, and without a word she opened the silver bag she carried and handed it to him. "You'll come in for something, won't you, Ross? Coffee—or a drink?" She plied her choices anxiously to his back as he bent to unlock the door.

He straightened, and in the light, Anne saw his eyes search out hers. He was waiting for her to add her invitation to her sister's.

"Yes, won't you come in?" Her words were cool and perfunctory.

His mouth twisted. The mocking glitter in his eyes told her he knew she didn't want him to stay. "Since you were so kind to ask—perhaps for a moment or two, if you're sure we won't be disturbing Owen."

"Oh, Daddy's probably gone to bed long ago," Shari assured him blithely as she shed her own coat and took his. "Anyway, he's used to things going on in the evening, my friends ringing at odd hours and things like that. He always says this is our home as well as his. Now, what would you like?" she said, taking his hand and leading him into the living room. "Scotch, wine, coffee . . ."

"Coffee is fine."

"I'll go see if Grace has any made."

Shari disappeared into the kitchen, and Anne was left alone

with him. He stood in front of the couch, watching her as if she were a small bird of prey about to take flight, his dark gaze burning over her. In fact, she had considered excusing herself and going up to her room, but—damn! He wasn't going to rout her out of her own living room. She sat down, her dress a red flame against the dark blue of the chair, and stared back at him defiantly. "Please sit down." What should have been an icy command came out as a husky invitation. "I'm sure Shari will be back in a few minutes."

He didn't move. "I want to talk to you."

"We have nothing to talk about." She tilted her head and kept her chin high.

"We have a great deal to talk about."

"I can't think of one single topic that we could safely discuss—" The ring of the phone interrupted her words. The ringing went on.

Ross frowned. "Aren't you going to answer it?"

A faint smile lifted her lips. "I can see you haven't lived with a teenager in the house. It's for Shari. She'll pick it up in the kitchen."

The third ring was cut off, indicating that the call had been answered. "You see?" she said.

"Magic," he agreed, and she had to steel herself against the lazy charm of his lifted lips.

To her relief he didn't sit down in the corner of the couch close to her chair. Instead, he wandered behind her to the table where the discus thrower rested. She watched him for a moment, but when he moved out of her view, she subsided into the chair and tried to release the tension in her shoulders. *Let him wander around all he liked. If he didn't care to sit down, that was his problem.*

"This is a beautiful piece of art."

She didn't have to ask him what he was referring to. She could imagine the scene behind her all too well, a lean clothed male as well-proportioned as the sculpture that commanded his attention. "Yes. It was done on commission by a man in Dad's plant."

"Is it blown?"

"No, it was done with a mold."

"Part of its charm is the subject. One thinks of women's bodies as lending themselves to the medium of glass more than men."

"Why do you say that? Surely there is as much beauty in the strength and grace of a man as there is in the curves of a woman."

"Beauty is in the eye of the beholder," he quoted softly.

Her hands clenched, and she gripped the upholstered arms of the dark-blue velvet and pushed herself up out of the chair. "I'll just go and see what's keeping Shari—"

She shouldn't have had her back to him. She never saw the hand that clamped down on her bare shoulder and swung her around.

"You're not going anywhere," he murmured gruffly and lowered his mouth.

CHAPTER SEVEN

Taken by surprise, Anne had no defense against Ross. His hand tangled in her hair and his lips explored hers leisurely, as if they were his to do with as he would. His mouth caused a heavy warmth to throb in her veins, a warmth that began when he pulled her close on the dance floor, a warmth that swelled and grew and robbed her of the desire to fight him. . . .

Her mouth softened and allowed him access. His tongue probed and possessed, making her cling to him. Her hands moved under his jacket to find the hard muscles covered with soft cloth. She had a wild desire to dig under the belt of his pants, find the tails of his shirt and bring them out so that she could touch that smooth male skin just as she once had. . . . She fought against her treacherous longings, a sound of protest escaping her throat. He lifted his mouth just enough to allow her to speak. "Ross, please, don't do this—"

"Why not?" he said, brushing his lips down the side of her jaw toward her throat. "We both want it."

A sudden bitter taste rose in her throat. Had that been his rationale ten years ago?

She braced herself and pushed at him. He allowed her to widen

122

the space between them, but he didn't let her go. His arms shackled hers against her sides, his fingers locked in a hard circle at the small of her back. "You're a curious creature."

"Thank you," she said, her voice arid.

"I thought I knew you—once."

She glared at him, her chin high. "But as they say, a lot of water's gone under the bridge since then, hasn't it?"

"Water?" An arched eyebrow mocked her. "Strange you should mention that. We made love on the water once. You haven't forgotten that any more than I have, have you?"

Her nerves leaped. "I'd forgotten it enough to become engaged to another man—"

"But not enough to go through with it. Three days after I arrived in Runford, his ring was off your finger."

"Because he was in love with another woman, damn you!"

"The little violin player," he said, watching her.

She stared at him, speechless, her eyes glittering. Ross had seen Jane's face last night just as she had. He was too damn perceptive. "It had nothing to do with you."

He said, his voice low, "I find that hard to believe after the way you kissed me just now."

Every fiber of her being screamed in anger. "Why, you conceited, egotistical—" The word to describe him accurately failed to come, and she trailed off into frustrated silence.

"Bastard?" he supplied helpfully.

"I wouldn't demean your mother that way," she told him coldly. "She died giving birth to you. She can hardly be blamed for producing an arrogant, loathsome man she never knew." She struggled to gain her release, but his hands only clamped tighter around her. Defeated, but not cowed, she shot him a killing look. "Let go of me."

"You don't want that. You want me to pull you closer and go on making love to you," he mocked.

After the kiss they had exchanged, she knew she couldn't deny that. "All right," she said, and was satisfied to see a flicker of surprise cross his face at her cool honesty. "I want you. But I don't love you."

For an unguarded moment she thought she saw that same flicker of pain burn in his eyes as it had at the Inn. "What's the matter," she taunted. "Don't you believe a woman can have desires that have nothing to do with her heart?"

"Yes, I believe it of some women." His eyes moved over her flushed face. "But not of you." For a long silent moment they stared at each other, adversaries locked in a silent battle of wills. Then something seemed to occur to him. "But there's one way to find out if you mean what you say." The tone was subtly challenging.

"I mean what I say," she said tautly. "I don't have to prove it to you."

He pulled her closer. "If you don't love me, then we can finish what we started ten years ago. And this time"—his eyes locked with hers—"we'll be on even terms. We're both adults now." Every word seemed calculated to wound her. "We can have an affair, and when it's over, we can both walk away—and no one will get hurt."

Her skin went cold. Here was the most neatly sprung trap of all.

"I don't have—affairs." Her voice seemed frozen in her throat.

His eyes burned into hers. "Then why not start now, with me? I'm the perfect candidate. I have no jealous wife, no children from a previous marriage, no wish for a more permanent arrangement that would stifle your career."

"It's out of the question." Frost tinged her words.

"I would say it's very much in the question," he countered softly.

"All other considerations aside, it's a little impractical, isn't it?" She tilted her head, pretending to consider it. "I'm going to Florida, and you'll be returning to California."

"What makes you think that?" The familiar mocking smile returned.

124

"Well, it's obvious—"

"Only to you. I have a completely equipped office waiting for me at my father's house."

"How convenient for you." She gathered herself to parry his verbal thrusts and protect herself from the pain he was inflicting on her. "If you really need a live-in lover to make your days in Florida complete, I suggest you ask about among the neighbors. I'm sure you'll find some female willing to spend her time in your arms." She paused and then threw a dart of her own. "After all, you are a rich man—"

His fingers bit into her bones, and she was pulled roughly to him. "I'm also a patient man," he growled, "and it's a damn good thing for you that I am." He captured her mouth, and all the tender care he had lavished on her a moment ago might have come from another pair of lips. This mouth ravaged hers, ground down on hers cruelly. She pushed at him, but there was no moving that hard body. He was all hard bone and muscle— focused on one thing, possessing her.

"I got a phone call from Heather, and then I had to make the coffee—" Shari's words ended in a shocked intake of breath.

Ross released Anne, but as if he knew she would need the support, he held her elbow. She turned to face Shari. The girl's face was white, and the small round tray she held in her hands looked as if it were in danger of sliding to the floor.

"Shari—" Anne stretched out her hand for the tray.

Shari backed away, looking desperately young. Her eyes were brilliant with hurt pride, and Anne's heart went out to her younger sister. "This whole evening has been a big joke, hasn't it?"

Ross moved forward and took the tray out of her hands. She watched him as he bent and set it down on the low table, a dazed look on her face.

He straightened and faced her. "There was no joke."

"Wasn't there?" Tears made Shari's eyes more vividly green. "You made me think you cared for me."

"I do," Ross said soberly. "I cherish you very much, Shari. You're the sister I've never had—"

Color swept up into her face. "I don't want to be your sister—now or ever." The tears that had glistened on the surface threatened to spill over. "Don't let me stop you," she cried. "Just go on with—whatever you were doing. I'll just get out of your way—"

The words disintegrated into sobs. She turned and ran for the stairway.

"Shari—" Anne cried out, but Shari was running, stumbling up the stairs, her breath coming in gasping sobs.

Anne twisted free of Ross's grasp and ran after her sister, taking the steps two at a time. But Shari was driven by anguish, and reached her room before Anne could catch her. The door was shut and the lock clicked.

"Shari, listen to me, please," she begged through the closed door.

The choked answer was muffled. "I'll talk to you in the morning."

"No," Anne pleaded, careful to keep her voice down to avoid disturbing their father. "Please, honey, let's talk this out now."

Silence met her words.

"Shari, please listen to me."

"Go away." The voice was calmer now, more petulant than disturbed.

"Anne." He had followed her up the stairs and now stood beside her, gripping her arm, turning her away from the door. "I may not live with a teenager, but I know enough about women to guess that you'd be better off to let her sleep on it and let her own good sense help her save face."

"Haven't you caused enough trouble? Just—go away." She shook her arm, trying to release it from his hard fingers. She didn't succeed. He tightened his grip and turned her away from Shari's door. "I've got to talk to you in private." As if he had known exactly where it was, he went unerringly to the door of

126

her room. He was brusque and cool, an impersonal executive managing a squabble among employees. It was only when they were inside and he pushed the door shut and enclosed them together in the softly lit room that she became aware of where they were.

She turned on him. "What are you doing?"

He was blunt. "Not what you think, obviously. I need to talk to you without the possibility of Shari overhearing, and this seemed as good a place as any." He relaxed back against the door, and his eyes traveled over her flushed face. "For God's sake, Anne, if I'm to have any kind of relationship with either of you, you've got to listen to me. Don't build this up all out of proportion. Shari is a sixteen-year-old girl with a harmless crush on an older man. She created a little fantasy, and now she's going through what most of us have gone through—at one time or another."

Anne grimaced. "You're only trying to ease your guilty conscience."

In the long, poignant silence, he stared at her, his eyes dark and dangerous. "If I have a guilty conscience, it doesn't involve her."

She fought down the leap of nerves at his deliberate reference to their lovemaking, and remembered who he was—and how he had betrayed her. A hard, curt laugh bubbled out of her throat. "Don't tell me you felt guilty about what happened between us."

Slowly he came away from the door, the relaxed look about his body gone. A hard look of purpose firmed his mouth, put a sheen in his eyes. "There isn't a day of my life I haven't regretted what happened between us," he said heavily, "regretted it—and wanted it to happen again."

She made an anguished sound and turned to the door, but he moved like lightning and caught her in the hard trap of his arms.

She strained away, pushing at his chest. "Let go of me."

"Let's talk about guilty consciences," he murmured, lowering his head to her bare shoulder and brushing his lips along the top of the bone, just as he had the first time he made love to her, "and conflicting motives." He raised his head and said silkily, "When you were out with Adams the other night, you wore a prim little blouse tied at the neck. But when you knew you'd be spending the evening with me, you wore this." He reached out and touched the silky material just between her breasts. "Don't you know you were inviting me to kiss you here"—he bent his head and feathered his mouth over the hollow of her throat—"and here"—his lips wandered a little lower—"and here"—his warm mouth trailed fire over the sensitive skin just above her breasts.

She wanted to push him away, she knew she *should* push him away. But her hands didn't seem to be connected to her brain. No part of her body was ruled by logical thought. His lips continued bestowing those enticing butterfly kisses on her, sending chills of sheer delight chasing over her body. She was like a person rescued from the desert, tasting the first sip of water after enduring unbearable thirst. Still she tried to resist. "Ross, don't."

He raised his head. "Stop saying things you don't mean," he muttered.

Her gasped protest only made it easier for him to clamp his mouth on hers and claim her with his tongue. Sensual warmth flooded her, centered in an ache at the base of her spine. He was bombarding her with sensations, the roughness of his jacket under her hands, the smoothness of silk underneath, the erotic probing of his tongue, the clean, faintly musky smell of him. She adjusted her body with a subtle movement, melting closer to him, giving him easier access to her mouth, sliding her hands under his jacket.

Locking her against him in the new position she had initiated, he lifted his head, and his eyes glittered over her heated face. "Should I tell you 'Don't, Anne'?" his low, husky voice mocked gently.

She made a movement as if to break off the embrace, but he held her in a steely grip and murmured, "You're not going anywhere."

128

His mouth came down on hers again, possessive but gentle, tenderly coaxing her response. Coherent thought vanished, and she clung to him and answered his gentleness with all the pent-up emotion she had been repressing for years. The lapels of his jacket were rough against her bare shoulders. She made a little sound of protest. "Your jacket—"

He held her with one arm and slid it off the other, then reversed the process, and the garment fell to the floor.

"Wouldn't you like to return the favor?" His warm breath laughed softly in her ear. She hardly heard him. She was totally engrossed in sliding her hands over his broad chest, discovering the corded muscles of his back, the hard outline of his bones. Her mouth sought the strength of his jaw, the tiny stubble beginning on his chin. She wanted more of him, so much more. . . . His hands went expertly around her, and with one smooth movement he slid the zipper of her dress down. The satiny material slithered away, and cool air fanned her heated back. "Ross—"

Her soft protest brought his comforting mouth to her cheek. "Shh." He flattened his palms against her naked back, and took away the chill. She wore only a pair of cream-colored lacy bikini pants, and he held her half-naked body against him as if he were absorbing her through his skin. It was so totally right that she should be in Ross's arms like this, having him hold her, touch her, comfort her. She was starved for him, and he was feeding her hunger. . . . Then he pulled away, and his eyes wandered over the smooth perfection of creamy breasts, the darkened peaks. She had invited him to look at her once before, and she faced him as she had then, defiant, proud, her chin high.

His hard face darkened and he shuddered and groaned. The hunger she felt was echoed in his eyes. With a swift, deft motion he scooped her into his arms and lifted her away from the tangle of red dress at her feet. He carried her over to the bed, placed her gently on the spread, and followed her down, half covering her with his body, kissing her eyes, her cheeks, her temple.

"Anne." He groaned her name from deep within, as if his emotion was too great to be released in a mere word. "You beautiful witch." He touched her gently, his fingertip brushing down the length of her from the sensitive hollow of her throat, between her breasts, and down lower to her navel. Her skin quivered and burned in its evocative wake. "Where is it—that heart that you keep locked away?" His hand cupped her breast. "Is it here?" He bent his head and lovingly kissed the taut peak that betrayed her arousal. His warm lips on her sent firebursts of feeling through her.

"I want it," he whispered. "I want all of you. . . ."

Her spirits soared—and then just as quickly plunged. He wanted her, but for how long? A day, a week, a month? Was she to amuse him until he went back to California and the arms of the lovely Nancy?

She lay very still, her head turned away. Then, bracing herself, she thrust him away. "No," she said. "I won't be a replacement for your—nighttime playmate."

Two dark spots of color flamed on his cheeks. "Is that what you think I want from you? One night of sex?"

"I don't think," she said, staring up at him defiantly, her eyes tawny dark, her hair spread like a fan over the spread, "I know. I've had experience with you—remember?"

He raked her with a scathing glance, but whatever he wanted to say he kept to himself. With a deliberate litheness of movement, he levered himself off the bed and picked up his jacket. He slung it over his shoulder and turned to look at her, his face cool and composed. She wrapped the spread around her and sat up, watching him.

Her attempt to hide her body from him brought a sardonic smile to his lips. But still he lingered, his hand on the doorknob.

"Well?" Her voice sounded strangely sharp in the intimate room. "What are you waiting for?"

He shrugged carelessly. "Maybe for truth to dawn," he said casually. His eyes locked with hers. "I am a patient man, but even I am beginning to wonder how long it will take." He opened the door and stepped out into the hall. When he closed the door behind him, she felt as if he had taken everything that ever mattered in her life with him.

From below she heard the sound of the outer door opening and closing. He was gone. She lay back on the bed, her body throbbing with a thirst that hadn't been slaked. She would block him out of her mind and out of her life. But the covers slid sensuously over her body, and she remembered the touch of his fingertip gliding from throat to waist—and shuddered. Like a ghost in the night, the vision of Ross rose inside her head. Her fevered body recreated the way he had held her, the way his hands molded themselves to her as if they remembered her more immature curves, the way his lips had been both demanding and tender. . . . She remembered, too, the way she had wanted the kissing and caressing to continue, ached for him to play the *Rhapsody* within her soul again. . . . Somewhere in the depths of her mind a voice whispered, *Why not? Why not take what he's so willing to give? This time you know it's only temporary. This time you're not a teenager with a starry-eyed dream of love. This time you'll be walking into it with your eyes wide open.*

No. I couldn't.

Why not? Because you're still in love with him?

No. No! Dear God, no. . . .

Anne was thankful she had no lessons on Monday morning. It was well after ten o'clock when she woke. Quickly she showered, dressed, and descended the stairs, knowing that if she didn't put in an appearance soon, Grace would be up pounding on her door. As it was, she braced herself for the woman's tart comment when she walked into the kitchen and poured herself a cup of coffee.

"A good strong cup of tea would do you more good, I'm thinking," Grace said sharply as she stood at the sink, peeling potatoes, the crisp white apron ruffle on her shoulder moving as she worked. "Have you come down with the flu, or are you still tired from Saturday night?"

"No. I just feel a little—washed out this morning, that's all. I overslept." She leaned back against the counter and lifted the cup to her lips. Coffee was the hot stimulant she needed to lift her spirits.

"Humph. In my day, a girl who was engaged didn't spend an evening with another man."

"I'm not engaged, Grace."

The woman turned slowly around and her eyes dropped to Anne's hand. "So you aren't." Her narrowed eyes searched Anne's face. "What happened?"

"He was in love with somebody else." She said it casually, not bothering to hide her indifference.

"And playing you for the fool." Grace's hackles rose.

"I think he really didn't know what he wanted." *How easy it was to be charitable when your own emotions weren't involved!*

Grace's mouth firmed. "Well, it's a good thing you found out now and not after you were married."

"Yes, isn't it?" she said, her mind wandering, trying to decide whether she should call Joel Winters, their solicitor, to see if he was certain he would have the contract ready by this afternoon.

"You don't seem too—upset."

"I guess I'm not, particularly." There was a short silence.

"When will you be leaving to see your mother?"

Anne shot her a look. "How did you know about that?"

Grace managed not to give way to the little smile that played over her lips. "Your father told me. He's hoping you might be reconciled with her, and I say it's high time."

"Grace—"

The older woman turned to face her. "Your mother was a fine woman, missy. And don't you think anything else."

"Please, Grace, don't start on me—along with everyone else." The weariness she was feeling crept into her voice. "Can't you

132

let me make up my own mind? I wasn't a child when Mother left. I know what she was like."

Grace was unmoved. "Maybe, maybe not. A child rarely knows what a parent is like deep down inside."

"No, a child mostly just knows whether a parent is around when the child needs him," Anne shot back.

Grace's eyes blazed and she started to speak, but then she seemed to think better of it. Her lips clamped together. "I'll not say another word. But I know the day will come when you'll regret your words about your mother."

She did not want to alienate Grace. The woman had been loyal to the Runford family for too many years to deserve anything but Anne's full respect and affection. "Perhaps you're right," she said easily, keeping the peace. "We'll have to wait and see, won't we?" She took another sip of coffee. "Did you talk to Shari this morning?"

Grace thought for a moment. "What talking there was, I did. She didn't have much to say."

"Do you think she was upset?"

Grace examined the potato she was peeling for anything unwanted remaining. "Yes, she was. But she didn't confide in me. Nobody does anymore."

Anne put her cup down and impulsively stepped to the woman's side. Her arms went around the shoulders that were straight with bruised pride. "You're a fraud," she said softly. "You know most things before they happen around here. Don't think I'm going to be tricked into feeling sorry for you." She laid her cheek against the woman's cool one.

A sound from Grace's throat was her only answer, but the housekeeper's face softened. Anne's gesture of affection had pleased her. "Whatever it is, Shari will get over it. She's young and resilient."

That afternoon, in her father's office, Anne thought about Grace's words and wondered why she couldn't have had more of Shari's resiliency. Even now, the casual way Ross leaned over the desk, gave the contract a perfunctory perusal, and signed his name sent a dart of pain through her, and in retaliation to the emotion she said sharply, "Aren't you taking a chance, signing something you haven't read thoroughly?"

He raised his head and gave her a cool look. From the moment he stepped in the office his manner had been impersonal. Those passionate moments in his arms thirty-six hours ago might never have happened. His ability to turn his desire off and on at will told her that his emotions were not any more involved now than they had been ten years ago.

"My solicitor called yours early this morning, and they reached an agreement on the exact wording of the contract." He handed her the slim black pen. "I have faith in the people who work for me."

She hesitated, knowing that she had been neatly outmaneuvered once again. If she took the time to read it, she was showing her own lack of confidence in her ability to instruct Joel. "It isn't necessary. Joel knew what I wanted."

"Yes, he seemed to," Ross murmured.

Careful not to brush his fingers, she took the pen from his hand and signed on the line below the dark scrawl he had made on the paper.

"I'll be leaving Runford in a half hour." There was a small clicking sound from the pen before he slipped it into his inside jacket pocket. He wore the same gray suit he had worn the first day she had seen him. "I assume a copy of the contract will be mailed to my office?"

"Of course."

His eyes took their full measure of her, flickered over the severe hairdo, the tailored jacket. "Back into your protective coloring, are you?"

She lifted her chin and stared back at him, her mouth tightly closed.

He straightened, as if he were tired of baiting her. "I'll return a week from today and, weather permitting, we'll fly to Florida that afternoon."

"But we may not be able to get tickets so soon."

He lifted his dark head. "You won't need tickets. You'll be flying with me." He paused and added, "And be sure to bring light clothing. It's summer in Florida."

When she got off the plane and walked out to the parking lot in Orlando to stand waiting for Ross to unlock the door of the silver-gray Thunderbird, it was indeed summer. The sun beat down on her head, and her body felt unaccustomed to the warmth that surrounded her. It seemed unreal. It had been a chilly twenty degrees and snowing when they left Runford. Here it was in the high eighties, and the breeze that caressed her face was heavy with warmth. She had worn a linen suit and a light coat to travel in the Learjet, but now, before she settled into the car beside Shari, she took off her coat and her jacket and laid them in the backseat, thankful she had had the foresight to wear a sleeveless blouse.

On the other side of the vehicle, Ross shrugged out of his jacket and tossed it on top of hers in the back with careless ease. When Anne and Shari were seated, he slid behind the wheel and reached in front of them to flip open the glove compartment.

"There are sunglasses in there for both of you. I had to guess at the style and color, but I thought for the short amount of time you will be here, my choices would be acceptable."

Shari's were oval, the lenses tinted a deep blue. Anne's had clear lavender frames with graduated shaded lenses.

She unfolded hers and slid them on her nose, thinking that his mind for detail had always been keen. She remembered playing piano duets with him at the cottage. She had the advantage with her greater technical skill, but if there was a change of tempo or dynamic she mentioned to him beforehand, he never forgot to add the nuance when they reached that spot in the music, as other people, even accomplished musicians, often did. Making

music with him had been almost as enjoyable as making love.
. . .

"You can tell us where we're going now, can't you?" Shari's face was turned toward Ross, her voice eager and excited. Back in Runford, waiting with Anne for the plane, she had been quiet and withdrawn. But the sight of the luxurious interior of Ross's executive jet had made her pique melt away. While Ross worked at paperwork at the round table to the side of them, Shari wiggled in the leather chair and looked out the window. It was difficult for Shari to remain annoyed for any length of time. Her natural exuberance was too bouyant to remain buried for long. Whether she had been acutely disappointed to find that Ross wasn't attracted to her, Anne couldn't really tell. Perhaps Shari missed having a male sibling, and Ross, having no brothers or sisters, had recognized Shari's need and responded to it. That was, at least, one tangle cleared away.

But now, in the car, speeding toward the meeting with her mother, Shari's throat tightened.

"Why don't you just wait and be surprised," Ross said smoothly, in answer to Shari's question. After that, a tense silence fell in the car that even Shari didn't lighten with more questions about orange groves and Florida.

Then, when they had left I-4 and were traveling along with the stop-and-go traffic on U.S. 27, Shari's attention was caught by a billboard. A young woman clutched a towrope as water spewed behind her.

When Shari exclaimed about it, Ross came out of his introspective silence to ask, "Would you like to visit Cypress Gardens?"

Shari admitted that she would and asked what the place was like.

He told her about the bird shows and the ski shows and the bougainvillaea that grew like a wall of blossom above the garden and its waterway canals.

"But do we have time?" Shari asked. "I mean if—" There was

a pause, and then she said the words as if they were foreign to her, "If my mother is expecting us."

"I mentioned the possibility that we might stop off at the Gardens if the idea appealed to you."

Anne looked out the window, but she saw nothing. Was Ross giving her a chance to collect her nerves before she met her mother? It didn't seem likely. And yet, if her mother was as anxious to see them as everything Ross had done seemed to indicate, his purposeful delay didn't make any sense.

Mentally she shrugged her shoulders. She didn't want his consideration, nor did she need it. She had spent a week preparing herself for this meeting, warning herself to expect nothing from it, knowing it was something she had to endure for the sake of the school.

A half hour later she had succeeded in clamping down on her emotions enough to present a cool, bland face to the world as they stood in line beside Ross, waiting for him to purchase the tickets, as he had insisted on doing. Inside, they walked down the grassy hill toward the big stadium that rose in front of them. Mercifully the sky had clouded over, and the sun appeared in intermittent bursts that would not burn their sensitive skin.

They decided to go directly to the stadium. Anne slowed her steps, letting Shari come between her and Ross. They climbed the outer stairs of the stadium, and when they reached the top, began to descend on the other side under the huge roof until they found a space toward the middle with a good view of the lake that would accommodate the three of them.

Several people were already seated on the concrete steps. They crossed in front of a man and his young daughter in order to reach the place they wanted. Anne, comfortable in the shade, gazed out over the water. It glistened with a clean sparkle that drew the eye. On the ski ramp, a long-legged crane had taken possession. He turned his head, looking about disdainfully as if to say he really didn't understand the antics of those strange two-legged creatures on the other side of the water.

As if he could recognize the signs that the show was about to begin, the crane flapped his wings and flew to safer ground. Boats and skiers moved into position and the show began. Young, sun-bronzed men did daredevil stunts over the ski ramps, executing daring head-over-heels flips. In contrast, a graceful ballerina climbed to the shoulders of a male skier and did a back bend over the palm of his hand as they skimmed over the water. Eight young women clad in red suits were a pleasing contrast to the blue water, extended shapely legs, their ankles in the towropes, doing ballet poses behind a slow-moving boat. The famous four-tiered pyramid carrying the flags that spelled out the words *Cypress Gardens* floated by, the four men skiers supporting three women on their shoulders, two more women above them, and the final courageous woman on top.

When the show was over, they walked leisurely through the botanical gardens and gazed at the cypress trees that were estimated to be sixteen hundred years of age.

"Cypress doesn't rot in the water," Ross told them. "Those trees can last forever."

"Nice to know there are some things that have a lasting quality," Anne murmured, feeling a stab of satisfaction as Ross's face darkened.

There was a little silence among them as they turned away from the trees to continue along the path that was bordered by low, flowering shrubs. Ross said nothing then, but when Shari walked ahead to examine the Florida pool, the one made in the shape of the state of Florida for an Esther Williams movie, he fell behind to grasp Anne's arm.

"I'm warning you," he said softly.

Her eyes flashed a warning of their own. "Am I supposed to be frightened by your threats?"

His eyes took a leisurely tour of her flushed face and ended at her mouth. It was as if he had reached across the stone path and touched her on the lips. "How incautious you are. You haven't changed a bit, have you?" His voice was low, unintelligible to the people around them.

She turned away, her quick stride taking her to the banyan tree that sprawled like a many-armed monster over the circular path around it. She concentrated on it fiercely, putting out of her mind the thought that Ross had reminded her of the afternoon she had thrown caution to the winds entirely. . . . The branches that grew over her head had perpendicular arms attached to the earth so that the parent tree looked as if it had given birth to many other trees, still connected to it. A tree supported by many root systems such as this one was would last forever. . . .

She continued to walk ahead of Ross and Shari, winding around the paths, scarcely seeing the luxuriant growth all around her.

When the path had taken them through the rose garden and brought them back to within a few feet of their starting point, Anne was more than ready to agree to Ross's suggestion that they have a snack in the dining room.

In a huge pavilion overlooking the water, they sat and ate hot, crispy slices of pizza and drank cold soda. A man and woman played and sang country and western music, their mellow voices keeping the crowd smiling.

The total effect was relaxing, and by the time they had purchased a funnel cake for Shari, a light, wafflelike confection with powdery sugar on top, and walked back to the car, she was pleasantly aware that some of the tension she had felt on the flight down and in the cypress grove beside Ross had ebbed away.

It was almost four o'clock when Ross left the main road past Punta Gorda to take a well-maintained, but little used spur of the highway. A sign at the end of this road advised them that Pine Island was seven miles away.

"Is that where we're going?" Shari asked.

"Yes," Ross said, volunteering no more information.

After another few miles, they crossed a bridge and were now, according to a sign, on Pine Island. It would have been difficult to tell otherwise. The tall trees made any view of the ocean impossible.

There were signs of many years habitation on the island. A café named Captain's Cove needed a fresh coat of white paint, but the place was well patronized if one could judge by the number of cars parked around it. A boy with his jeans rolled up to the knee walked along the road, carrying a string of fish, his face berry-brown from the sun.

In contrast to the older section of houses and small grocery and bait stores, newer lush homes lined a canal that angled off to the right. Sleek powerboats and cruisers cradled in hoists provided their owners with instant access to the sea.

A turn to the right kept them sheltered in the forest pine that grew in the sandy soil of the island. Bougainvillaea bloomed a deep rose color in one of the many vacant lots that were advertised for sale. An attractive house of dark logs built on stilts was also available for sale or lease. Street names were peculiarly blunt: Dead End Road, Dead End Street. Anne supposed that were true of every street, except the one they had entered the island on.

A turn to the left brought them a view of the ocean. It was utterly calm, a placid turquoise. They had reached the northernmost tip of the island. They were close to their destination.

A feather of tension moved inside Anne as Ross pulled up to a white house that faced the sea. It was more imposing than any of those around it, although it appeared to be the same general age. Three balconies jutted from the two-story structure, one on the front and one on each side. A long extension of the house gave it the appearance of having been built to accommodate servants. White board fencing enclosed the yard, and a sign warned Ross not to turn around in the adjacent yacht club driveway.

He stopped the car, took a key from his pocket, and unlocked the latch on the gate. When he had driven through, he left the car once again to fasten the gate securely behind them.

The sleek automobile rolled to a stop in front of the door, and Anne could no longer put off the inevitable. Her heels sank into the sandy ground, but overhead, tall trees provided a pleasant shade. Like the sea, the air was almost too heavy with moist heat. Perhaps it was her own state of mind that gave the atmosphere that feel of the calm before the storm.

Ross unlocked the trunk and took out their luggage. A man-servant appeared at the door of the porch and came down the steps toward them.

"Good afternoon, Mr. Leyton." The speaker must have been twice Ross's age, a tall, heavily-built man who managed to convey a leashed strength. Even though he was of the age to have a thin cover of white hair on his tan head, a ragged scar on his cheek told Anne he was a man who knew something about defending himself. She supposed he was as much a bodyguard as he was butler. The dark bands above the elbow that held the long white sleeves of his shirt in place were incongruent, more so than the dark and impeccably tied tie. "Mr. and Mrs. Leyton just went out for a short cruise. They will be sorry to have missed you."

Ross seemed unperturbed. "It's just as well. I'll show our guests to their rooms, Charles, if you'll see to the luggage. I'm sure they will welcome the chance to freshen up a bit."

Anne expected the man to answer "Very good, sir," in the best tradition of butlers, but Charles merely nodded and tucked her tan suitcase under his arm.

Knowing that her mother was not in the house made it easier to climb the steps to the porch and stand under the protection of the balcony to wait for Ross to open the door.

The interior was shadowed, cool with air conditioning. They followed Ross down a hall and into a living room where bare wood floors and delicate lace curtains gave the conflicting impression of light and space amid the clutter of homey furniture.

A deeply comfortable leather couch and a matching lounge chair were grouped around a fireplace, and the walls were lined from floor to ceiling with books. An open stairway curved above, and Ross, after pausing a moment as if to make sure no one was seated in the room, began to move up the stairs with surefooted ease.

Shari had been uncharacteristically quiet, but when Ross opened the door and said to her, "This is where you'll be staying," she stood as if stunned for a moment and then burst into speech. "What a fabulous room. How did Mother know I love wicker things?"

"We did a little research," Ross returned lazily, his eyes moving past the girl's shoulder to Anne's face.

The room was done in cool whites and greens. Two queen chairs with their high fan backs stood on each side of a round glass-topped table. A free-standing mirror was framed in an oval of wicker, and the large double bed with its green silk spread had a heart-shaped lacy headboard.

"It's a dream room," Shari exclaimed. "I could stay here forever."

Her sister's words sent an unpleasant little shaft of jealousy straight to a vulnerable spot. For the first time Anne understood why separated parents vie for the attention of their children. A year ago, when Shari had outgrown her childish decor, Anne had worked for weeks, painting and shopping for curtains and furniture, consulting Shari on every detail—but still conscious that she must stay within the confines of a limited budget. This room had been done without a thought to the cost.

She lifted her eyes and found Ross watching her. For a second a harsh emotion flared to life in his eyes. But when he turned to Shari, his voice was bland. "Have a rest and freshen up. I'll call you when your mother returns. Right now I want to show your sister to her room."

Across the hall, she followed Ross into a world created from a monochrome scheme of blue. Directly in front of her, the huge expanse of canopied bed riveted her inspecting gaze and created an awkward silence as she stood looking at it, unbearably conscious of Ross turning to see her face. But still she couldn't look away. The blue spread exactly matched the shade of the rug; the bed seemed to be floating on a sea of blue. Achingly conscious of Ross beside her, his body still and hard with waiting, she turned in an attempt to put the bed out of her vision and out of her thoughts and glanced around at the rest of the room. Sheer blue drapes hung at the sliding glass door that very probably led out to a balcony. A love seat covered with white velvet was the only relief from the overall sensation of being immersed in the sky. Even the chest of drawers and the dresser had been lacquered to match. On the dresser sat a piece of pure Venetian crystal, a vase she recognized as being antique and very valuable with its flanged lip and intricately crinkled edge. It held no bouquet; it needed nothing to enhance its beauty.

She fought the urge to bolt from the room and crossed the soft carpeting to stand in front of the glass doors. Her fingers pushed aside the curtains. The balcony, easily the size of a small dance floor, was surrounded by a white lattice railing that was opaque. The railing was almost chest height.

"Someone must have been very safety conscious," she said, more to break the taut silence that permeated the room than to satisfy her curiosity about the house.

Noiselessly he moved behind her. The prickling feeling along her spine told her he was only a hairbreadth away. "Safety conscious?" Mild amusement lurked in his tone.

"The high railing," she told him, wondering why he suddenly seemed obtuse. "Isn't that a little unusual?"

"Can't you guess why it's like that?"

She puzzled over the hint of mockery and decided her thought processes must be as distracted by his nearness as her breathing. She couldn't think what he was alluding to.

"The former owner was a sun worshiper," he said. "The balconies were constructed for private sunbathing—in the nude."

143

An urge to escape the lushly erotic bedroom and her own thoughts made her fingers move to the door. "Is there a view?"

She fumbled with the clasp until Ross's hand reached around and pushed her away. "Yes."

The catch released, and the door slid back with a soft *woosh* of sound. She stepped over the threshold, the heat that surrounded her a surprise, an indication that her body had adjusted quickly to the coolness of the air-conditioned room. The floor was carpeted with a sturdy indoor-outdoor rug in a brick-red color. There was a round patio table with an umbrella shading the black wrought-iron surface, and a lounge chair in readiness. A clear vision of Ross stretched out on that chair, his naked lithe body as lean as a lazy panther's, every inch of him bronzed by the sun, rose out of her subconscious to taunt her. She clenched her fingers into fists and took the five steps that brought her to the railing, hoping the view might distract her.

The ocean was the same pale color it had been a few moments ago, the sky arching above in a bluer tint. In the distance thin, high clouds drifted—and a cruiser floated on a leisurely path toward the shore.

She stood, her eyes riveted on the clean, beautiful lines of the boat, and knew without asking that her mother was on that vessel. The welling of tears made her vision blur.

"She's out on the deck," came the husky voice behind her. "She's waving to you. Lift your arm, damn you."

For a moment her confused senses simply couldn't assimilate his words. Ross made a rude, impatient sound and grasped her elbow. His unrelenting grip on her forced her hand aloft while he kept his own hand out of sight below the railing.

She saw her then, the woman who seemed very little different from the mother she remembered knowing. Leora Leyton, standing on the deck of the boat, excitedly waving her arm, was clearly visible, a trim woman wearing white pants and a brief red blouse, with a matching scarf over her dark hair. Despite herself, Anne opened her palm and waved back.

144

The cruiser, in a sudden burst of speed, rode beyond the point of the island and out of her sight. She felt the tension in Ross's grip slacken, but he did not let her go.

"I'd like to wring your sanctimonious neck," he growled and used his hold on her arm to twist her around toward him. She was caught between his hard body and the railing of the balcony but, unwilling to let him glimpse her vulnerability, she kept her long lashes lowered. "Let me go."

No form of escape was to be allowed. *"Look at me, damn you!"*

She raised her head, her eyes glittering with her tears. Her chin high, her body rigid, she said, "What else do you want from me? Haven't you done enough?"

His heated gaze scorched over her liquid eyes. The color drained away from his tan face, and the muscles in his cheeks strained under an intolerable tension. "Oh, God." He pulled her into his arms and muttered in a low, agonized voice she hardly recognized as his, "Forgive me. Please, forgive me." He lowered his head and buried his mouth at the side of her neck.

CHAPTER EIGHT

The sun blazed down, but the heat Anne felt was not from its warmth. His hands were moving over her shoulders, her hips, her spine, and his mouth was buried in the soft skin at the side of her neck, his lips nuzzling the hairs that had escaped her chignon. Her mind whirled. Was he asking her to forgive him for condemning her without justification just now? Or for that dim and wonderful past where he had been hers for a pulse of time? Why should she forgive him for something that had been the sole sum of her existence, the only time in her life she had felt truly alive?

Under the onslaught of his hands on her body and his mouth on her warm skin, she couldn't think why he would want her forgiveness. What was there to forgive between two people who belonged in each other's arms, whose bodies fit together with an old and remembered ease?

Her mouth moved over his jaw, his cheek, his nose, and at last found the lips that had the power to lift her to a height of yearning she had never reached with any other man. She leaned against him, hungry for the feel of his body against the length of her thighs, the bones of her hips. He readjusted his stance to partially support her, his mouth discovering hers with tender possession, his tongue flicking lightly against her teeth. She could feel the passion rising in him and the heat of his body and she knew that soon they would both be beyond denying the desire that was rapidly rising out of control.

Still kissing her, he pulled the pins from her hair. When the tawny waves fell free around her shoulders, he made a muffled sound, like a low groan, and released her lips to turn her slightly. His hand moved between them, and the buttons of her blouse were loosened with a trembling urgency. No thought of staying his hand entered her head. She was on fire, the need to feel his touch burning through her. Expertly he loosened the front clasp of her bra and, in one smooth movement, covered her breast with his palm. His fingers played with it lovingly, circling around the sensitive center, teasing, enticing. Exquisite pleasure sent fire along her veins; a delicious sense of anticipation tautened the rosy bud.

But the delight had only begun. Now he bent his head, and his mouth followed his fingers, its warm moistness creating new rapture. While his mouth claimed her, his tongue coaxed and wooed and discovered each tiny crevice, each intricate design. He was an instrument of lovely torture, his lips and tongue and teeth creating an unfulfilled need deep inside her. When she thought she would cry out with wanting, his mouth left her breast—only to travel across her, his hair brushing erotic patterns against her naked skin as he sought her other breast. The moment his lips touched its trembling curve she was swept up to that same height of aching need and heady fulfillment. He made her desperately hungry for him, and satisfied her all at the same time. She moved her hips against his and clutched his broad back, wanting more, wanting to be closer, wanting to absorb him into her heated skin. . . .

"Anne. Anne! She's here—mother's here. Anne, where are you? I can't wait—I'm going down."

Shari's voice from inside the house was a jarring intrusion that

147

offered only a brief interruption. She clung to Ross, willing him to make her body sing with the same ecstasy as before, but it was he who froze and clasped her upper arms to hold her away.

In the hot sun a breeze rattled a palm tree, making it rustle with a dry, papery sound. He stared down at her. "You're like a potent tropical drink," he murmured. "You go right to my bloodstream. I've never gotten you out of my system."

"Ross—" She leaned toward him.

A shudder shook his entire body. His breath came heavily, hard. "We can't go on like this," he muttered, his voice hoarse. "We're tearing each other apart."

She looked up at him, the enticing beauty of the curves he had caressed still partially visible under her loosened blouse. Intuitively aware that he still was not fully under control, she said huskily, "Do you have a solution?"

Perspiration stood out on his brow. "Yes. As soon as I can arrange it, I'm leaving."

Like a wave destroying patterns in the sand, his words washed like an emptiness through her. "History does repeat itself, doesn't it?" Her words were cool, bitter.

His face tightened and his fingers punished her arms with an even more constraining grip. "Damn it, Anne! What do you want from me? You've already refused to come to my bed. There's nothing left for me to do but to get as far away from you as possible. It's the only way I'll preserve my sanity."

"I don't want you to go." She raised her palms, and the hold he had on her didn't prevent her from finding the male nipples under the thin fabric of his shirt.

He looked at her, his mouth hard, his eyes blazing, but he didn't push her away. Another long, silent moment passed. The breeze had died away. "Then come to me tonight."

The moisture left her mouth and throat. She let her tongue dampen dry lips, and he watched her, his eyes cataloging every movement of that red tip. "All right," she whispered, and the thunder of heated blood seemed to roar in her ears at the sound of those two words in her own voice.

She thought he would pull her into his arms and kiss her. He didn't. His face was hard, unreadable. If he was pleased about her decision, he gave no sign of it. It was as if he had turned to granite. He was still, like a panther watching its prey. Then he released her arms and said curtly, "Your mother is anxious to see you. I'll go down and tell them you're on your way."

His casual acceptance of her willingness to give herself to him chilled her heated blood as nothing else would have. She watched him pivot and stride through the door he opened easily. Curtains billowed inward, telling her that he had, in his instinctively courteous way, left the door open for her. But he had slammed that other door, the door to his heart, without a second thought.

Inside the bathroom a few moments later, she pressed a damp cloth to her cheeks. The water that came out of the faucet was very little cooler than her heated skin. She forced herself to raise her head and look into the mirror. Her makeup was gone, her hair in loose abandon around her face, her lips swollen with the imprint of Ross's mouth. Staring at the woman in the mirror, she knew she had done what she had vowed never again to do.

She had given her heart back into Ross's keeping.

A muffled cry escaped her throat. She bent her head, splashing her face with the tepid water, a fierce determination filling her. She would not let Ross's unemotional acceptance of her agreement to stay the night with him make her change her mind. She would take what had been hers to take years ago. Ross didn't love her—but in some strange way their lives were tied together. They had been, right from the very first, even though he couldn't make a permanent commitment to her. Now, for one night, or for whatever number of nights he allotted her, he would be hers. And for the rest of her life she would know that for a few brief hours she had lain in the arms of the man she loved.

She wasn't sure how she found the courage to dress, reapply

her makeup, and walk down the stairs toward the room with its sound of animated conversation.

Then she was on the bottom stair, and a quiet fell.

She saw her mother first, still wearing the same white pants and red blouse, her hand resting on the shoulder of a man, a man who looked enough like Ross to leave no doubt in her mind that this was Carson Leyton—a man who sat in a wheelchair.

"Anne." Her mother's voice was low, emotion-ridden. "Oh, it's so good to see you."

After the first moment's hesitation, Anne took a breath and crossed the room, her nerve endings telegraphing the message that Ross lounged in a corner of the sofa next to Shari, a glass in his hand, and that he was watching her with heavily lashed eyes. She came close to the woman she had once known so well and held out her arms. "Hello, Mother."

Her mother's face blazed with relief and delight and she stepped into Anne's embrace, her arms encircling her grown daughter. A faint scent of the sea clung to her mother's clothes, along with the scent of a perfume Anne was unfamiliar with. The feel of those bare arms and firm body was achingly familiar, though. She remembered the warmth and glow her mother emanated—as if Leora Leyton were always more vitally alive than other people.

The older woman held her away and gazed at her with avid eyes, eyes brimming with tears. "How beautiful you've become."

"Beauty is in the eye of the beholder, so I've been told," she said easily, and knew her arrow had reached its target when she heard the slight movement of Ross's body on the leather cushion.

"I might be a bit prejudiced about my daughters," Leora admitted, her head to one side, a smile revealing even teeth. "I'll ask an impartial judge. Carson, aren't my daughters beautiful?"

"In my completely objective opinion, I would say they are, indeed, beloved," Carson Leyton concurred in a low voice Anne remembered well.

"You—remember Carson—" Leora's natural poise seemed to

desert her momentarily, but Anne had regained hers. She held out her hand. "Yes, of course I do. Hello, Mr. Leyton."

"Anne, my dear, it's a pleasure to see you again." There was something in his eyes, a watchfulness. Was he gazing at her to assess her reaction to his infirmity—whatever it was? His tall body had a healthy look about it, almost as if he were malingering, using a wheelchair for no reason at all. The short sleeves of his tan shirt exposed arm muscles that looked rock hard.

"May I get you something to drink?" Ross's voice was cool and cutting as he rose to his feet and moved to the bar that had been opened out from one of the bookcases behind them. "Gin and tonic?"

"Yes, that's fine, thank you."

He mixed her drink quickly and efficiently with the ease of long practice and handed it to her, his face utterly impregnable. Whatever thoughts he entertained were severely guarded behind those hooded eyes, that disciplined mouth, the lean, cynical face.

"Do sit down, Anne." Her mother became the anxious hostess, aware that there were tensions in the air and determined to dispell them. Her quick, telling look at Ross betrayed her reading of his tone of voice, the look on his face as he handed Anne her drink. Another stab of unreasoning jealousy pierced her. Her mother had come to know Ross well in the years that had been denied her. . . .

But thoughts like that were self-defeating. She had no right to think them. She tilted her chin upward and moved with an unconscious grace to settle into the deep luxurious cushion on the other side of Shari. The spacious couch gave her ample room. Ice cubes tinkled in her glass as she brought it to her lips to drink. The twist of of lime gave it a cool, refreshing scent and taste that she needed badly. Her nerves felt torn and heated; her body still throbbed with reaction to Ross's lovemaking, so that she had a fine-tuned awareness of everything around her, the cool draft from the air conditioning, the way the sun was dropping in the sky, its lengthening rays giving the room a golden glow. And most of all she was conscious of the acute attention she was receiving from Carson Leyton. He had his son's ability to look deeply at a woman, or was it the other way around? He had even dropped those muscular arms to the wheels of his chair and with a quick, unobtrusive movement, turned his chair slightly to give him a better view of her.

"Did you have a pleasant trip?" he asked conventionally, but Anne knew the thoughts that were going on behind that probing gaze were not conventional at all. What was the man thinking?

"Yes, thank you," she said, balancing her glass between her fingers on the side of the rounded leather arm, "very pleasant. Your son has been most—kind." She turned her head to look at him, her mouth curved in a mocking smile. He had not returned to his place on the couch, but instead stood leaning against the balustrade of the stairway, his position keeping him just out of her vision unless she turned her head. His face was still glacial.

Carson Leyton continued to ask her questions until gradually the conversation became more general. Her mother and Shari entered in, and the talk flowed smoothly after that initial bit of awkwardness, but though she talked about the school, and told them something of her talented pupil, Dina, she couldn't rid herself of those antennae that stayed tuned to the man who stood silent and still just out of her view.

She sipped her drink, but this time its bittersweet tang brought no relief from the tension that held her in its grip. If anything, her nerves seemed to stretch to an even more brittle state, and by the time they had agreed it was time to change for dinner, and parted to go their separate ways, she was more than glad to place her glass on the low table, climb the stairs, and escape the sight of Ross's dark, sardonic face.

An hour later, after she had showered, washed her hair, and brushed her teeth, Anne felt marginally better. Her clothes had been unpacked and shaken free of their wrinkles and were now hanging in the closet. She put on the wisp of a strapless bra, its flesh color making her look nearly naked, and matching bikini panties. She had already decided what to wear. She went to her closet and brought out a simple aquamarine silk sheath, with cap sleeves and a deeply veed neckline and low-cut back. She slipped it on and tugged at the silken material, which balanced precariously on her shoulders, exposing a smooth, provocative triangle of creamy white throat and neck, and the delicate curve of breast—too much so to allow the wearing of a conventional bra. The full skirt swirled around her knees and showed a generous portion of her long, sleek legs.

Green and gold eyeshadow gave her eyes a mysterious allure. She touched up her hair with a curling wand, her mind reverting to the scene downstairs an hour ago. What ailment confined Carson Leyton to a wheelchair? Was this the reason Ross had carefully guarded the location of their whereabouts? Companies, especially those built on the reputation of one man's business acumen, could collapse overnight if it became generally known that the head man's health had failed.

She laid down the wand, her eyes thoughtful. Was Ross actually in control of the entire operation? She lifted the sable brush with its light rose lip color to her mouth—when a knock sounded on the door. It wasn't like Shari to knock, but perhaps it was because the girl was in a strange house. Anne said, "Come in," but didn't turn.

The moment the door opened and closed with a silence that was almost stealthy, she knew it wasn't Shari who had entered her bedroom. With a strange prickle of excitement raising the hairs on her arm, she lifted her eyes to meet Ross's glittering gaze in the mirror.

"What"—the words wouldn't come out—"what do you want?"

A faint sardonic smile lifted the corner of his mouth. "That should be obvious by now, shouldn't it?"

She circled around to face him, her color high. He leaned his hips against the door and folded his arms, a man so at ease in his body that even the beige linen jacket and well-fitted black trousers looked casually comfortable on his lean frame. Again he wore no tie, a triangle of dark hair exposed at the open neckline of his cream silk shirt. The sight of him in the softened light of her bedroom made her say sharply, "I hardly think you came in here to ask rhetorical questions. Would you please say whatever it is you have to say and get out?"

She twisted back to the mirror and lifted the sable brush to apply the red lip color, and then realized her hand wasn't steady enough to draw the brush across her lips. Damn him! Why couldn't he leave? He had his pound of flesh. Did he want a pound of soul, too?

"Would you believe I have nothing particular in mind to say to you?" His voice was a husky mock of amusement. "I was walking down the hall with every intention of passing by your door when I was struck by the uncontrollable urge to see what you were wearing this evening."

"You don't expect me to believe that." Resolutely she kept her back to him and steadied her little finger on her chin to trace the outline of her lips.

"No," he said huskily, "you don't believe anything I say. But I think you'll believe this—that as much as I enjoy looking at you in that dress, I'll enjoy removing it from your body even more."

She fought the reaction of her quivering nerves to his words and sat like a stone on the bench. Her ears, always acutely attuned to him, caught the soft sound of his tread on the carpeting. He was walking toward her. A flood of anticipation and desire and wild excitement mingled in her veins. When a fingertip probed the V-shaped neckline at the back of her dress and she felt his warm lips whispering down her exquisitely sensitive backbone, the flood turned into a deluge. She gasped, and the sable brush slipped. "Don't do that."

His soft laugh mocked her. "You've already agreed to let me do much more than this to you tonight."

Wildly she twisted around to him and half rose—until she

154

realized that standing would bring her within an inch of his mouth. She sank back on the seat.

Looking down at her, taking every line of her defiant, angry face under his scrutiny, he seemed amused. "You've smeared your lipstick," he said blandly.

"No thanks to you," she said, her voice edged with tension and sarcasm and a wild, aching need to have him touch her again.

"I can remedy that." He pulled her onto her feet, crushing her against him roughly, but once she was in his arms his grip loosened slightly and his lips on her mouth were anything but cruel. They were tender and persuasive, demanding their own sweet retribution—her unrestrained response. She fought the battle from without and within valiantly, but after a microsecond of resistance, the warmth of his mouth and the insistent wooing of his tongue breeched her barriers, and she relaxed and took what he was offering her. Then he gained possession of all the dark sweetness of her mouth, and she could resist him no longer. She met his intimate kiss with a wanton response, her own tongue taking erotic liberties with his until she heard the low moan of pleasure in his throat. She moved closer, her body singing that old and ancient music. He shuddered and lifted his head.

"I have a feeling," he said, still holding her, his hand gently pressing her head against his chest, "that this is going to be one very long evening."

A wild urge to flee him, to run far away and hide the truth of her love for him, made her pull away. One look at his face told her he knew exactly what she was thinking. "Oh, no," he warned softly. "Not now. You're not escaping this time. This time we'll play it my way." He grasped her hand and towed her toward the door.

"We're going down—together?"

"Why not?" he parried.

"Your father—"

"—knows enough to mind his own business," he said bluntly. "Unless you're concerned about your mother—"

"My mother's opinion means nothing to me."

His eyes darkened. "I was proud of the way you handled yourself this afternoon. Don't disappoint me this evening."

"My family affairs are none of your business," she retorted.

He gripped her arm and forced her to walk with him across the blue carpeting toward the door. "Anything that concerns my father's happiness and well-being is my business."

There was no opportunity to answer him. They were out in the hallway now, and he allowed her to step ahead of him and begin the descent down the stairs.

Everyone else was waiting in the living room, Shari in a cream dress, a ruffle at the round neck, and the full skirt accented with a rope belt, her feet in sandals that laced up her bare legs and made her look like an attractive country girl. Her mother wore a sleek red dress with a mandarin collar and tiny fluttering sleeves that left her arms bare. The slitted skirt showed an expanse of silken-clad thigh. Even Carson Leyton had dressed for the occasion, his jacket a brown linen that suited his aristocratic good looks and contrasted with the full head of white hair combed back from his forehead.

Leyton favored his son and his wife's daughter with a shrewd glance. His eyes flickered past Anne to Ross and then back to Anne again. It was only then that she remembered she had forgotten to reapply her lip gloss. She had no idea what she looked like, but no one seemed to find anything unusual about her appearance. Her mother complimented her profusely.

Ross refused Leora's offer of a drink, and Anne copied his example, knowing that if she didn't, dinner would be delayed. As if he had been waiting for just that, Charles appeared to announce that he was ready to serve them dinner.

The dining room was done in cream and pale yellow, with the warm pecan color of country French chairs and a high sideboard gleaming in the light of the chandelier. There was no chair at the

156

head of the table; Carson Leyton expertly wheeled himself into place there. Her mother at the opposite end, Shari beside her, Ross pulled Anne's chair out for her, placing her between himself and his father.

The centerpiece caught her eye at once. In a low gilt tray a rough piece of branch stood like a miniature tree, and clinging to the juncture of its two branches was an orchid. Not the large kind she had often seen in florist's shops, but a smaller, more delicate specimen. Deep purple petals looked like velvet in the soft light, their texture contrasting beautifully with the rough brown bark. The arrangement had an oriental quality about it, as if great care had been taken in every detail.

She wanted to ask her mother about the work of art, but before she could do so, the first course, a savory onion soup, was served in thick pottery bowls with handles. Charles distributed the appetizer with a quiet efficiency that Anne knew Grace would have admired. They were well into the main course of chicken cordon bleu when her mother turned her head to Anne and asked pleasantly, "How is Sheldon Morrison?"

She nearly dropped the fork she was holding. For a moment the blood thundered in her ears. Why hadn't she anticipated that her mother would ask about the beloved professor who had urged Anne to pursue a concert career?

"I really don't know. I—haven't seen him for a number of years."

Now it was her mother's turn to be startled. "You're not studying with him now?"

"No, I'm not." Anne fought to keep the emotion out of her voice.

Her mother hesitated and then said, "May I ask why?"

Anne's appetite vanished. "There wasn't any future in it."

A shadow crossed her mother's face. "I see. You plan to devote your life to teaching?"

"Yes. I'm luckier than most," she added carefully. "I enjoy working with children."

"And this—Dina, I believe you said her name was. Does she have the talent to go on to the concert stage?"

Anne relaxed slightly as the subject of conversation turned away from her personally. "I believe she does. She has all the behavioral traits she needs to take her straight to the top."

Carson Leyton gave her a piercing glance. "Behavioral traits? I thought one needed prodigious amounts of musical talent to be a performing artist."

She put her fork down to look into Carson Leyton's face, her own earnest. "Most people do use the word *talent* when they talk about artists, whether in music or the visual or verbal arts. I happen to believe talent is nothing more than the right combination of personal traits that drive a person toward the effort and sacrifice of time it takes to achieve excellence in an art career."

Carson leaned back and gave her his full attention, and for the first time understanding for her mother filled her. Even confined to a wheelchair he exuded charm and the indefinable quality of male sexual appeal. She could feel the double-barreled effect he must have had on her mother in his prime, with his ability to focus his entire attention on a woman, and that subtle message of male challenge added to his charisma. He must have been irresistible—as irresistible as his son. . . .

Carson said, "I'd be interested in hearing what those traits are."

Anne couldn't repress a smile. He was all executive curiosity, a man accustomed to listening to others to learn about new ideas. "Prioritized, I assume."

His easy answering smile was so full of charm and so like Ross's of ten years ago, it nearly paralyzed her. "You can enumerate them in any order you care to."

"All right." She took a breath, suddenly aware of the quiet attentiveness on the other side of her. Ross, too, had the ability to listen carefully. "I'll try. The problem is, some of the traits are conflicting. An artist needs the discipline to practice constantly on the same repetitious exercises—and the courage to experi-

158

ment, to push himself to stretch and try new music. He needs the ability to make himself the center of his universe and focus in on his faults and weaknesses in his playing, and he needs to have a keen knowledge of the rest of the world, the heights and depths of the universal emotions that all the great composers infused into their music. An artist needs intelligence and drive—and luck, the good fortune to be born into a home where parents give loving support at an early age for the pursuit of excellence. Some of the programs that focus on young children—the Suzuki approach—the Orff method, have shown us that the sky's the limit in what children can learn—if they are taught with love and skill."

"Do you have young students at your school?"

Anne nodded. "We have an Orff instrument class, and several violin students who study privately using the Suzuki method."

Shari made a restless movement in her chair, and Carson Leyton turned his attention to her. "Are you a musician, my dear?"

"No." Shari seemed unperturbed by the question.

Anne slanted an amused glance at the young girl. "She has an interest in the theater—and a marvelous gift for mimicry." A teasing gleam sparkled in her eyes. "She even does impressions of musical instruments."

Shari colored and then looked at Anne and laughed. Anne couldn't repress her own low chuckle.

"I think that must be a private joke, Carson," her mother said, her voice tolerant.

"Evidently," he agreed. "Every family has those."

Carson asked Shari about the plays she had done, and under the cover of the conversation, Ross said softly, "I wonder what instrument Shari does best. A cello, perhaps?"

Despite the huskily intimate voice and her response to it, she smiled . . . and the slow, lazy smile that was her answer was so breathtakingly intimate that she was sure everyone at the table could see the charge of light and heat that suffused her. But the arrival of dessert created a diversion. It was a light lemon mousse, a lovely combination of tang and sweetness, and when she put down her spoon and sat back, she knew her sensual enjoyment of the sweet was being noted by Ross. Color bloomed in her cheeks again, and when Leora suggested they have their coffee in the music room, she was only too glad to rise from her chair and follow her mother down a hallway toward the back of the house that ended in a room that appeared to be set outdoors. The walls were glass and soared up to a cedar-beamed ceiling. Tall pines and low-growing shrubs offered complete privacy. Modular furniture covered with cream-colored velvet was grouped around a huge table. Delicate cream-colored drapes were pulled to one side of the west wall, offering the option of privacy, and in the corner of the room stood an ebony grand piano, its lid raised.

The music room. Why hadn't she guessed? She had been distracted by that moment of intimacy with Ross. She flexed her fingers, praying her mother wouldn't. . . .

"This is Ross's favorite room," Leora said, settling herself into a chair next to her husband. "You will play something for us, won't you, Anne? I've been—hoping you would."

Eyes nearly the tawny color of her own entreated her silently. Her mother was asking for more than just a performance at the piano. Leora was asking to share a part of her life again—a part of her life that she had kept precious and private after that disastrous summer and fall.

While she hesitated, Charles appeared with the coffee and began to serve it out of the silver pot into delicate china cups. Anne accepted one from him, hedging for time. "Perhaps you should ask Ross to play."

"No," he said softly, standing beside her, taking the cup from her hand. "Play the *Rhapsody* for your mother."

She saw it then, the bright gleam of challenge in those blue-gray eyes. He was fully aware of what he was asking. He was putting her to the final test, telling her to bestow the final forgiveness on her mother by sharing with Leora the wild joy of the *Rhapsody* that she had created for him that night in the dark, yet moonlit recital hall.

She didn't move. Quivering with nerves, her eyes locked with his. A strong urge to break away from that mesmerizing gaze and sink into the velvet softness of the nearest chair washed over her like a physical pain. Long years of wanting to lash out in hurt and despair couldn't be erased in a moment. But she couldn't move away from Ross's eyes, either. Something compelling and real reached out to her from those blue-gray depths, and she couldn't move, couldn't turn away. "Play it for her," came the low command that still, somehow, left the final decision to her.

Under the spell of his warm voice and the probing gleam of subtle challenge, the last barrier crumbled. She loved Ross desperately, loved him now, just as she always had. It was herself she needed to forgive—that impetuous seventeen-year-old who had begged a man to make love to her. She had believed she was condemning her mother, when in reality, she had been condemning herself. Now, after all these years, it was time to deal with her mother compassionately—and have a little compassion for the young girl who had seduced her only love.

In a voice husky with emotion she heard herself say the same two words she had said to him only a few hours ago. "All right."

What his reaction to her affirmation was, she would never know. She turned away from him and walked across the bare wood floor to the red velvet piano bench. With trembling fingers she pulled it out and settled herself. She was frightened—not because she was going to play, but because the protective walls she had built around her heart were gone. She had faced the truth about herself. But what would happen when the time came for her to leave her mother—and Ross? Could she bear to be permanently separated once again from these two people she loved?

She found the sustaining pedal with her foot and pressed it experimentally, a sudden flood of life and strength filling her. She still had her music. She would find an inner source of strength—and she would concentrate on her career and she would survive. She had survived before, and she would again. Her strength would come from knowing that she had faced the hurt and anger and despair and anguish and guilt inside her—and released it all.

She looked down at the piano keys. She would give them a gift, these two people she loved so much. She would give them the gift of herself and the music that until now, had been her own private refuge.

It would not be hard to perform well on this piano. The Steinway name gleamed above the keyboard, and the bass keys would have that characteristic full sound that would make the intricate harmonies of the *Rhapsody* even richer.

When the first sonorous chords reverberated through the room, her fingers faltered on the keyboard. Her anxiety to play well was inhibiting her. Then, as she listened to her own playing being enlarged by the excellent acoustics, and realized that the piano had one of the finest registrations she had ever experienced, she regained her confidence, and the music began to soar and glimmer with nuances of emotion. The sound transcended notes and chords and became something else entirely, a living thing with a life and soul of its own, the lyric parts more tender than she had ever allowed them to be, the crisp chords brilliant and powerful. The music took on dynamism and a glowing, shimmering radiance that only fed her with the hunger to create more of its gossamer beauty. She was pouring her soul into the music and she was more vulnerable at this moment than she had ever been in her life.

Suddenly it was over. She dropped her hands into her lap, and felt drained and empty. A silence fell in the room, and for a moment she thought she had failed miserably. Then they began to applaud, the sound echoing peculiarly in the glass-enclosed room.

Leora came to her and reached for her hands. "My dear." Tears glistened in her mother's eyes. "What can I say? It was beautiful—beautiful." Then she held Anne's eyes with her own and said quite simply, "Thank you."

Her mother's hands were warm—and dear. "It was my pleasure—Mother."

The question asked, the answer given. Leora's face looked lit from within with her joy, and that bright look sent a depth charge of emotion through Anne as she sat on the piano bench, gazing up at her mother. Those warmly familiar hands had a touch like no other's—a touch she had never forgotten. All the bitterness, all the lonely memories, seemed to melt away under the touch of those strong fingers. She seemed suddenly whole, the lonely, confused teenager she had been finally at peace with the mature woman she had become.

"I have one more request." Her mother's hands tightened on her own, as if she knew her request would not be pleasing. "Let me hear you and Ross play something together—like you used to do at the cottage."

In an instant the euphoria of the moment was gone. She pulled her hands away from her mother's. "I—couldn't. I'm sure I've forgotten the music. . . ."

Leora turned to plead her case to Ross. "Don't you think you could remember one of those duets you used to play?"

"I could try." He didn't move from his lazily relaxed position on the couch. "But frankly, Leora, I think anything would be an anticlimax at this point."

"Nonsense." Leora was undeterred. "All recitals end with a light, familiar encore."

"I never was in Anne's league as a pianist, and I'm more out of it than ever now."

His reluctance made Anne flash him a cool, challenging look. "You must remember 'Country Gardens.' We played it enough times." *Let him wriggle out of this one.*

He met her eyes across the low back of the furniture. "I might be able to find a few of the chords."

He placed his coffee cup on the table and, with deliberate ease, rose and walked toward her.

His hip rubbed hers as they positioned themselves on the bench. Ross had always played the left-hand parts, since they were generally easier, but that gave him the responsibility of operating the sustaining pedal, and now, as he extended his foot to it, she could feel that long length of leg and thigh touching every inch of hers through her chiffon skirt. "Ready?" he asked.

That husky, deliberately baiting tone intensified the sensual impact of his body next to hers. She fought down the sensations that were tingling through her side to every other part of her and began to count. It had always been her job to signal when to begin, and she tried not to think about how easy it was to remember all the rituals they had worked out.

The minute they began to play she knew she had been tricked again. Ross remembered every chord as if he had played the music yesterday. He had demurred on purpose, knowing she would insist on their playing together. *Damn the man! He knew her so well.*

Nothing could have been further from the emotional intensity of the *Rhapsody* than the light, bouncy tune they were playing now. Happiness and a rhythm for dancing bubbled through the sound that filled the room. Though Ross's technic wasn't equal to hers, he kept a rock-steady rhythm, and they achieved a good duet sound, avoiding that quarter beat imprecision that marred most amateur duet playing.

She tried to avoid looking at his hands, but she couldn't. They were there in front of her, just below the beige linen sleeves, well-shaped wrists ending in masculine fingers sprinkled with dark hairs, the nails clean and blunt, their tips finding the chords with the same ease that they had glided over her body. . . .

Her heart rocketed, and she hit a discordant note. Beside her, Ross murmured one word. "Yes."

She knew what he meant as if he had said it aloud. Yes, he was having trouble concentrating, too. Yes, he was disturbed.

164

Yes, he remembered caressing her, holding her, making love to her. The fact that he shared her thoughts brought her no pleasure. Those thoughts were motivated by desire, not love. And perhaps he, too, had his own feeling of something uncomplete, a thread of his life left hanging.

She felt a stab of pain that seared into her soul. Was he going to make love to her to absolve his own feeling of guilt? He had said she was like a potent tropical drink. She was in his bloodstream . . . and he must surely want her out.

The music ended, and Leora and Carson and Shari applauded, but all she could think of was her need to escape. She wanted to be away from Ross, away from that male magnetism that drew her like a moth to the flame and was just as unfeelingly destructive. She looked beyond Carson Leyton to the out-of-doors, where tall trees sliced the last rays of the sun into shafts of gold. In moments the day would be gone, and the night would follow. . . .

"Anne, dear, let me call Charles and have him bring you some more hot coffee." There was more than the kindness of solicitous hostess in Leora's voice. There was the concern and caring of a mother.

But she was beyond a mother's care, now. She was a woman—a woman who loved a man . . . who didn't love her.

Desperately she searched for an acceptable excuse to leave the room. She had to get away, to sort out the thoughts of how the evening would end—unless she changed her mind. She could always change her mind. It was a devil's bargain at best, and it could be rescinded. But if his body touched hers again, she would never be able to deny giving him what had been his from almost the beginning of her existence.

She rose from the piano bench, her breathing short, her nerves quivering with awareness of him. He remained sitting on the bench behind her. "I think"—she took a breath, but it wasn't nearly enough oxygen for her suffering lungs—"what I'd really

165

like to do is explore the island—if you wouldn't mind." She directed her words to Leora.

Ross rose, and she could feel the muscles of her throat constrict. Would he offer to walk with her?

"No, of course I don't mind if you want to walk for a bit, dear. But it seems a shame to have the party break up so soon. Ross, you'll have another cup, won't you?" Leora persisted, but as he rounded the bench and came into Anne's peripheral vision, she could see he was shaking his head.

"I've got work to do." His gaze swung to Anne, and she could no longer avoid meeting his eyes. There was not a glimmer of personal interest in them. His face was bland, his mouth cool. She might have been a stranger he had met casually that evening. "Have a pleasant walk." With a nod of his dark head to his father, and a smile directed at Shari, he went out of the room.

CHAPTER NINE

Outside, the air was cooler. The breeze lifted the skirt of her dress and whirled it sensually around her legs. She wasn't dressed for walking, she knew that, but she didn't want to go upstairs and run the risk of confronting Ross. She wasn't sure where his office was, but she hadn't seen it downstairs, so she was fairly certain that it had to be on the second floor somewhere.

She opened the gate with the key Leora had given her and crossed the road. The yacht club would no doubt consider her a trespasser, but the building and parking lot seemed to be deserted anyway, so she slipped out of her high-heeled sandals and let them dangle from one finger as she picked her way across the sand to the shoreline. That, at least, was public.

Coarse shells and stones had washed up and made the walking less than pleasant under her nylon-stockinged feet. She angled her path more toward the west and walked closer to the water. There, the sand was softer. The breeze whispered in the pines, and she took a breath, liking the mixture of resin-scented conifers and the fishy tang of the sea.

She wandered slowly along the edge of the ocean, knowing that the sun would soon be down, knowing that she wouldn't be able to stay out much longer, since she wasn't that familiar with the island.

But she needed breathing space. The scene in the music room had shaken her. She had crossed a boundary in her own life—a boundary between dreams and reality. She had dreamed of seeing her mother again, and thought those dreams would never come true. Now they had, and she had made her peace with her mother—and with herself—by playing the *Rhapsody*.

But she had dreamed of seeing Ross again, too. In her dreams, he had always taken her in his arms and kissed her and told her that he loved her. The reality was that he wanted—*needed*—an affair to get her off his mind. The cruelty of it made her head reel. How could she bear to let him make love to her when she knew he didn't love her?

The sun was almost gone, the sky purple. She should go back. But instead she walked on and rounded a curve on the island. That was when she saw it. Riding high in the water, its prow glistening white in the last light of day, the cruiser that rocked in the water in front of her was the same fishing boat Carson Leyton had brought so skillfully up the St. Lawrence River that afternoon while she waited breathlessly on the dock.

The sight of it knocked the breath from her lungs. It looked exactly the same; its clean lines were still beautifully simple, and its fiber glass body showed no signs of water damage or wear. The graceful curve of its prow still supported that fine wire railing, and the tinted glass in the engine room was still clean and transparent.

It bobbed at the side of a long dock, and as she stared at it her brain began to function. Her mother had waved to her from the deck of this boat this afternoon. She hadn't recognized it then, she had been thinking of other things. Now her body screamed with the urge to walk down the length of the dock and board the boat. She needed to see it, needed to know if the inside was as unchanged as the outside.

Not even stopping to consider the rightness or wrongness of

it, she climbed the step to the dock, her knees wobbling with the sudden jolt of adrenline in her veins. Her shoeless feet padded silently down the long length of wooden boards.

She reached the boat and clambered over the side, the fiber glass cool under her hands. The boat took her weight with a slight adjustment of its position in the water, and as it rocked, Anne steadied herself with a hand against the side. The carpeting had been replaced with a newer, sleeker floor covering. She remembered sliding to her knees on a hard, scratchy surface when Ross had shoved her aboard. . . .

A sound over her shoulder made her turn, but by now the dusk had turned to night. She couldn't see anything in that purple darkness. She hesitated, knowing she really didn't have the right to go below. But she was here, and that nameless need inside her kept her moving forward.

She reached down and grasped the heavy metal ring, half-expecting the hatch to be locked. It wasn't. It swung up easily. Then she was on the steps and moving down.

Below, she fumbled for the light switch she knew was on the wall and prayed that Carson Leyton had left the generator on. He had. At the upward movement of her hand, light flooded the room.

For a moment she simply stood and stared. Everything was different, and she wasn't sure whether that made her relieved— or disappointed. The flowery cushions were gone. The luxurious lounge was done in earth tones of amber and gold, the topaz color of the rug echoed in the drapes at the tiny windows. The couch had been covered with an ocher velour, and brilliant blue throw pillows provided contrast. The dark walnut paneling remained, but above it was a painting that might have been done by a pupil of Van Gogh's, brightly vivid with yellows and blues and greens, its subject a young girl with honey-colored hair, running across a field of tall grass.

Suddenly the boat swayed in the water. She clutched the side of a velvet chair, her heart going like a triphammer. Was someone coming on board? She would be well and truly caught if there was. There was no path of escape but back the way she had come. She stood statue-still, listening, waiting, but she heard nothing. She chided herself, thinking her guilty conscience was making her imaginative. She took a step, her heart beating at an even faster tempo. She had one last odyssey to make, one more ghost to dispel. There were more steps to descend, more light switches to find as she walked past the eating nook and the spotless galley toward the bedroom tucked under the bow of the boat.

The room she had known was gone. This room had been done to harmonize with the outer living quarters. A cream-colored velvet spread replaced the silk one she remembered, and a mud-colored carpet covered the floor, while pillows the color of sand and red clay were propped along the wall beside the bed.

Suddenly her sixth sense told her she was no longer alone. As if to confirm the crawling sensation at the back of her neck, she felt that slight rocking motion again. Someone was on the boat with her. She whirled, every muscle tensed for flight. A bulky body stepped into the bedroom, blocking her way, hard hands reaching out to catch her shoulders.

She fought and twisted, but her assailant's grip was like steel. She raised her foot and was placing several well-aimed kicks at his shin when a startled male cry to stop split the air, making her look into the face of the man who held her captive. It was Charles.

For a moment they stared at each other, two animals at bay. The coiled strength of his body was still ready to lunge; his hard face was still cool with purpose. And she was only too ready to fly at him again. He had been braced to take on whoever was inside this room, and he couldn't adjust to the fact that it was her he was holding and not some marauding criminal.

At last her outraged expression seemed to penetrate, and he dropped his hands from her shoulders. "Miss Runford—I'm sorry."

All at once she remembered he was not a young man. "I'm the one who owes you an apology," she said quickly. "Is your leg all right?"

Ruefully he leaned over and rubbed it. "It will be in a day or two. I'm just glad you weren't wearing those pointy heels women usually wear."

Lord! Her shoes! She must have put them down when she turned on that first light switch. She really looked as if she had made herself at home. He straightened and politely didn't ask why she was on board, but the question was there in his eyes, and she did owe him an explanation, at least. "I—wanted to look around the boat. I never thought about anyone—watching. You —saw the lights, didn't you?"

A slight smile cracked the hard mouth. "I thought it was a pretty shoddy job of theft if they needed to turn on every light in the boat, but"—he shrugged and his smile widened—"these days there's all kinds of incompetents around."

"I'll leave at once."

He didn't argue with her, and in the next moment she understood why. "Not that I don't want you here," he told her kindly, "but your lights might attract someone else with unsavory things on his mind."

She gave him a shaky laugh and turned to walk out of the room. "I could always give him a good swift kick in the shins."

"Yes, I'm sure you could." From behind her, his voice was gruffly amused. "But let's not take the chance, shall we?"

He turned out the lights while she picked up her shoes. Topside, he helped her out of the boat and had made another amusing comment that had her laughing, when a dark figure moved out of the woods.

She tensed, but Charles gripped her arm. "It's all right," he said softly. Then he called out, "It was only Miss Runford, sir. She was looking around the boat."

The figure stepped out of the darkness, and in the faint light reflected off the ocean from the moon, she saw that it was Ross,

171

and that he had taken off his jacket. His light shirt made his upper torso a beacon in the night.

"Leora told me you were out here. You shouldn't have gone alone, Charles. It could have been a gang."

"If it had been, I would have come back for help." Charles was matter-of-fact.

"You don't get paid to take unnecessary risks," Ross went on relentlessly.

Charles retreated into a dignity that seemed at odds with the toughness underlying those hard muscles. "Yes, I know that." There was an awkward silence.

"I'll see that Miss Runford returns to the house safely." Ross's voice was brusque. "Good night, Charles."

"Good night, sir." Charles took the curt dismissal stoically and strode to the end of the dock to walk past Ross and disappear into the darkness.

Suddenly conscious of the fact that her shoes were in her hand, she set them down on the dock and, balancing herself precariously, managed to slip them on her feet. Her heart was doing an arhythmic dance in her chest that did little for her equilibrium. Her poise was not helped by the fact that Ross had mounted the steps and was walking down the dock toward her. Beside her, his hand on her arm was steadying and yet earthshaking. "Are you all right?"

"Just a little shaken up," she said, hoping he would believe it was because of her encounter with Charles rather than her accidental meeting with him. "I'll be fine once I get back to the house."

The wind whispered through the pines, and the breeze lifted her chiffon skirt. The ocean lapped gently at the shore with a faintly primitive sound.

"You're not going to the house," Ross said softly. "You're coming back to the boat—with me."

She lifted her chin, and the breeze swirled the tawny length of her hair around her head. "No, Ross."

172

Only the dark outline of his face was visible, but she heard the sardonic disbelief in his voice. "No?"

"I've changed my mind. I think it's time we—let the memories go. We've got to realize that it's too late to recapture the past—"

Without another word he scooped her off of her feet and into his arms. "But it's not too late to go forward into the future."

She did not demean herself by kicking and struggling. With the solid warmth of his chest next to her ear, his hands holding her easily, she struggled only to retain her reason. "Ross, put me down."

He didn't slow his purposeful steps. "No," he said. "Not now—not ever."

Not ever. A mind-boggling thought. But of course he didn't mean it.

He seemed to. He didn't put her down, even to climb over the side of the boat. How he managed it she wasn't quite sure, but he was caught in a dark mood of determination that drove him forward—and struck a chord of wild exultation in her.

She let him bear her to the hatch. He was forced to let her slide to her feet then, but he kept a firm grip around her waist as he pulled the door open. He wouldn't have had to. She wasn't going to run away. She knew this was the confrontation they both had to face before they would be free. "Go on down." His voice was harsh.

She ducked her head and went down the stairs, picking her way carefully with her unsuitable shoes. He turned on the lights and pulled her across the length of the lounge, toward the steps that led past the dining nook—to the bedroom. "This time, we'll dispense with the coffee."

His voice was so flat, so matter-of-fact, that for the first time fear touched her, a fear that ignited anger.

At the brink of the steps, she turned on him. "Stop manhandling me as if I were a woman you'd paid for the evening's pleasures."

"But I have paid, haven't I? I'm paying damn dearly for your

173

lover's school. Well"—the tan hands began to unbutton the top two buttons of his shirt—"now you're going to show me what he's taught you."

She took her stand, her eyes tawny dark, her hands clenched. Because she was so furious, the truth came blazing forth. "He taught me nothing." Her body shook with the double shock of anger and pain. "I never let him make love to me, because I couldn't, because in ten years I haven't got you out of my head or my heart! Oh, God—I'm obsessed with you." Her face in an agony of pain, she met his eyes with a brilliant flare of pride in her own. "But I'll get over you—if it's the last thing I ever do, I'll forget you—"

She twisted and lunged past him for the steps that would lead her upward to freedom. She never made it. His hard hand on her arm whirled her around. She was brought up sharply against him, locked in his arms, his grip on her bone-wrenching. "Anne!"

She beat at his shoulders, his back, his chest, anywhere and everywhere she could reach. He was the enemy, and she wanted to be free. "Let go of me. I hate you. . . ."

Her words were raspy, frantic, but he only tightened his hold. When at last she paused for breath, he held her eyes with his and lowered his mouth to hers.

"No—" But her protest was far too late. He kissed her with a fierce energy that was white-hot, a consuming fire. All the pent-up emotions of the years spilled from his lips to hers, and in one blinding instant she knew that whatever her obsession was, his was greater; that whatever pain she had suffered, he had suffered as much.

She couldn't withold her own response from the maelstrom of his demand. She answered his wild, exultant kiss with lips just as eager, just as demanding. He was asking the question, and she was answering, every movement of her mouth, every answering teasing motion of her tongue telling him she was his.

His breathing was ragged when he lifted his head. "I was

174

sure"—the words were hoarse—"that when you sat there so damn coolly discussing teaching with my father, you were thinking of Adams—and wishing you were back there with him—"

"You were jealous." The truth vibrated through her like a breeze through the pines.

"That night at the Inn when I first met him, do you remember? I watched you giving Hutch dark looks because Adams was attentive to her, and I nearly went out of my mind."

She shook her head, her hair grazing his cheek. "Even then I wasn't jealous of her because of Michael. I was jealous because I thought that you and she—"

He was exultant. "—were lovers?" His husky laugh didn't deny it. "I'm glad you suffered a little. You deserved it. I could have killed you at the dinner table tonight. I had made love to you on that balcony only moments before, and you knew I planned to finish what I started before the night was over. Yet you sat through the evening cool as ice."

"I didn't feel cool as ice," she murmured. "You made my temperature shoot out of sight."

He pulled her closer and clasped his hands at the back of her waist. "Tell me you love me."

The husky urgency of his command sent a thrill of elation through her, but she thought of his attractive assistant and said, "After ten years, Ross Leyton, I think it's about time you admitted that you care for me a little."

"Care for you a little! My God, woman! You must know I do. Do you know I nearly ordered Nancy to stay in Runford to provide a distraction for Adams?"

"Would she have liked that?" She nestled against him, glorying in the warm feel of his body against hers.

He chuckled, the low sound vibrating against her breasts. "She might have been amused, but her husband certainly wouldn't have been."

"Her husband? Oh, you beast. You let me think you and she—"

He stopped her protest with a kiss. When he released her mouth, she said, "Ross—please. I have a right to know what happened all those years ago to make you change your mind."

"I didn't change my mind," was his astounding answer. "I never have. You were my first love—and my only love."

"But—"

A finger on her lips stopped her. "Do you trust me?"

Gray eyes met tawny gold ones with an intensity that burned. "Will you," he said softly, "believe me when I say I never got your message until it was too late?"

"But I tried for days—"

"I didn't know that, because I was locked up in a cell in a small town in northern California."

Her eyebrows flew up. "Locked in a cell—"

"Jailed for drunk and disorderly behavior." He gave her a lopsided grin that made her heart turn over. "Remember, I didn't know you had called. I was sure you had come to your senses and discovered you didn't love me after all, that you were too young and had too much ahead of you to tie yourself down to me. I knew, more than anyone, how much your music meant to you, how talented you were. I was sure you'd finally chosen your music over me. I had half expected it, braced myself for it, prayed it wouldn't happen. Anyway, I was in pretty bad shape the next day and in no mood to go to the office. I talked Tom Ewing, a friend of mine, into going for a trip with me, by car, up the coast. That night, we were drinking in a small country bar, and I got drunk—very drunk—and decided I wanted to play the piano. Tom tells me I was determined, too damn determined. The piano player was equally unwilling not to relinquish his place on the bench. We had a little—disagreement—and I sat down beside him and shoved him off the bench. I don't remember too much after that, but I think it was a rip-roaring good fight."

"But afterward—why didn't you contact me?"

Gazing down at her, his teasing look faded. He was silent for a moment. Then he said in a sober tone, "That's something I can't explain." She made a movement as if to pull out of his arms, when he said, "Someone very dear to you could have been hurt if I did. Please, darling, just—trust me and—let me love you—as I want to. As I've always wanted to. Now."

They gazed at each other again for a long, breathless moment. But even though she could feel the tension in his body and see the torment in his face, he let the slight distance between them remain. He was giving her the choice. She could take that final step of loving him, trusting him. Or she could turn and walk away.

She stood looking at him, letting the moment lengthen. She had no choice but to believe him. To turn and leave him now was unthinkable. She reached up and traced her fingers over the deep line on the side of his mouth. "It doesn't matter now, does it—as long as you love me."

If she had any lingering doubts about his love for her, the look of relief and exultation that swept over his face and blazed in his eyes erased them. He picked her up and walked easily down the small stairs, turning his body to negotiate the narrow doorway to the bedroom with her in his arms.

Two steps brought him to the bed. "I want to do this right," he said through gritted teeth, holding her, his eyes devouring her, "but I'm not sure I can wait—"

"It doesn't matter," she whispered back, her voice soft and melting. "I'm very good at practicing things I don't get right the first time."

His throaty laugh filled the small room and eased the tension, and her heart filled with joy and love for him.

He laid her down gently on the bed. His fingers shook as he held her up to reach the zipper at the back of her dress. With one fluid movement he pulled it down and then, lovingly, he pushed the silky material aside, making it fall away and expose her creamy shoulders. He leaned forward, brushing first one rounded bone and then the other with a featherlight kiss. Quickly, before she had recovered from the tingling pleasure of his mouth on her naked skin, her dress was lowered to fall loosely around her waist. His hand traced along the top of her bra, slowly, slowly, around to her back. The clip gave under his expert fingers, and the lacy garment was tossed away. Freed of the nearly transparent lace, the soft mounds quivered under his gaze, and though his whole body was trembling with need, he slowly and carefully cupped her breasts, letting his fingertips wander over the slopes, tracing down the valley between, teasing and tantalizing her, coming close to the dark rosy peaks, only to circle around and drift away until she ached for his intimate touch. She moaned softly, in an unnamed pleading, and at last, granting her unspoken wish, he leaned over and took her nipple in his mouth, his tongue rolling erotically around the taut bud. She moaned again, but this time it was a sound of satisfaction, as his sensual nibbling sent depth charges of desire through her.

Restlessly she reached out for him. Her hands encountered the silky strands of his hair and gave her palms sensual pleasure. She explored the shape of his head, the round curve of his ear.

He levered himself away from her to tug at his clothes. She shook her head and whispered, "Let me do it." He had already unbuttoned the top two buttons of his shirt in his first angry demands, and the dark silky hairs at his throat beckoned her. She finished unbuttoning it and pulled it away from the waistband of his dark trousers. The sight of his tan chest with its sparse covering of dark hair was just as disturbing as it had been those years ago. If anything, he was harder, leaner now, more supple— more male.

"Talk to me, honey," he ordered her, his voice husky and disturbed, his eyes brilliant with desire as he gazed down at her. "Tell me what you're thinking. Let me have your—your mind and heart as well as your body."

"I was thinking about you," she whispered, "thinking how beautiful you are."

Carefully lifting her, his hands cupping her buttocks, he pulled

178

her dress out from under her. "What a lot of nonsense you talk. I'm not beautiful."

"Beauty is in the eye of the beholder," she said huskily, teasing him, her eyes glittering as she watched him strip her hose away and kiss the length of her smooth thighs, bare to his seeking lips. "Were you really thinking about me when you stood in the living room, looking at the sculpture of the discus thrower?"

"What do you think?" He raised his head and moved to bury his mouth between her breasts, teasing that silky skin with his tongue. "I was visualizing you here, like this, naked and pliant and ready for love. The vision did nothing for my peace of mind, believe me, which was why I lost my temper with you a little later."

His hands caressed her, trailing over her breasts, wandering lower to her navel, and down to the soft feminine core of her. A sunburst of delight exploded inside her. At her slight gasp, he let the delight spin on, making her body writhe with desire. With eager, shaking hands she unfastened his belt and slid down the zipper of his trousers. For a moment he was stilled, then a low chuckle sounded in her ear. "I'm surprised you didn't think of that when you were seventeen."

"If I had, I wouldn't have hesitated."

"You're a witch," he murmured, helping her. "A beautiful, enticing witch."

"Then you're surely a warlock. Because I've been obsessed with you since the ripe old age of thirteen."

"I wouldn't believe that," he said, lying down beside her in his full and naked glorious maleness, his hand claiming her breast, "except that I remember the first summer I really knew I was in for trouble. You were about fifteen then, I think, and just beginning to change from a child into a woman. We were out fishing, and you had caught a big one. You were so excited, you stood up—"

"—and promptly fell out of the boat," she finished. "Yes, I remember."

179

"I pulled you out, but I was more disgusted than anything—until I got back in the boat beside you and saw how wet your T-shirt was and how you weren't wearing a bra . . . and I wanted you then, right there. It was not one of the best moments in my life."

"And what about now?" she asked, suddenly tired of talking about the past. "Where does now qualify in your catalog of moments?"

He was still for a second and then murmured in her ear, "Ask me after I've made love to you like this for a hundred years. Then I'll know."

He wanted her desperately, she knew that, and he would have taken her quickly, but his love for her and his tenderness, his concern for her pleasure, made him slow his responses, control his need. Propped on his elbow, lying next to her, he began to explore her body; his fingers lovingly brushed aside a tendril of tawny hair to make the shell of her ear accessible to his fingers. What a mystery it was that a man as strong as Ross, with such passionate needs, could touch her so tenderly. She had not known how sensitive that particular curve of her anatomy was, or what rockets of feeling could soar through her at the touch of his tongue on the intimate hollow. Those gentle hands wandered lower, brushed across her throat, traced a path between her breasts and below them to come up on the other side in a tantalizing circle that delighted as it teased. "Pearl and cream," he murmured, leaning over, his lips against the hollow of her throat, "and as sweet as I remembered." He nuzzled the vulnerable place where her life pulse beat, his mouth sending quivers of pleasure from her skin to a deep center at the base of her spine. Aching to give some of that pleasure back to him, she touched his head, discovered the indentation at his nape, stroked the crisp, vital hair, and then let her hands wander down the silky back to the leanness of his hips. He was warm and real and vitally male, not a dream. Never a dream. He—A sharp gasp escaped her as he took a rosy peak into his mouth. The tip of his

180

tongue was moistly smooth against her. The need deep within her sharpened, focused. As if he knew exactly what she was feeling, his hand found the source of need and tenderly eased it.

She clung to him, the muscled shoulders and smooth back her only anchor in this storm of desire. She let her fingers trace his body on a sliding path that took her palms around to the hair-crisp skin of his chest. He groaned in response and his mouth met hers. Sensual pleasure flooded every cell of her body. His lips left hers to play over her body once more while his hands continued to stroke and tantalize. The lovely torture went on relentlessly. He gave no quarter, allowed no amnesty. She was his, and every movement of his hands and mouth took his possession to a deeper, more primitive level. On the very edge of the chasm, she cried, "Ross—"

He moved over her, his weight heavy and erotic against her breasts, her stomach, her thighs. "Anne, oh my dearest Anne," he murmured, "I've wanted you for so long." And then his thrusting entrance brought the relief that she sought, the ecstasy she remembered. She took him in like an enclosing flower starved for the rain. His warm mouth closed over hers. Together they moved in the slow dance of belonging, first one choreographing their movements and then the other. She was filled with a sense of belonging, a sense of completeness. He was hers and he always would be. He went on filling the emptiness of her until their dance became an electrifying celebration of love that took them up to the heights of ecstasy.

Lying beside her, he played with her hair. "Do you know, no one in the world has the exact same color of hair that you do? I used to look for it on the streets in the foolish belief that you would come to California, looking for me."

"I nearly did, dozens of times—but I was afraid. I was sure you thought I was too young and inexperienced for you. I believed you had forgotten me entirely."

"I tried a hundred ways to put you out of my mind." The

words were spoken with a husky emphasis that told her how impossible it had been. She turned to him, tracing a finger over his mouth and nose, telling herself that she was really here on the bed beside him and that it wasn't a dream. She felt lazily sated, complete. But there had been so many long, lonely days, and he had assuaged his loneliness with beautiful women.

"The others meant nothing to me. None of them had a tenth of the impact in my life that you had." He turned his body to trap her legs under his and put a long, possessive arm over her bare body just under her breasts. "We're going to be married as soon as it can be arranged." He waited, watching her.

The words brought a shiver of haunting memory—that just as suddenly faded away. She knew he was waiting, watching her, waiting to see if she trusted him enough to say yes. She looked down at his arm, the bare leg that pinned her on the bed and tried to lighten the mood by teasing, so arrogantly male. "You have me in a very compromising situation, Mr. Leyton."

He raised up and glared at her, and in the soft light of the cabin, she could see he was trying to keep his face from betraying his relief. The tension she had felt in his muscles drained away. But he demanded her final commitment. "Just say yes, damn you," he growled.

"Yes, damn you." Her feminine growl was as accurate an imitation of his as she could make it, but her eyes sparkled with laughter and love as she met his fierce, slicing gaze.

A low sound escaped his throat that was neither a growl nor a groan, and he leaned over and kissed her, a fierce searching kiss. Then he rolled away from her and came to his feet beside the bed. She looked at him, unashamedly glorying in his male perfection but missing his warmth beside her. Lightly, teasing, she said, "That's it, then, just—a proposal and back to work?"

He leaned over her once again and gave her a faintly satanic smile. "I'm thirsty, aren't you?"

Before she could agree, he was up and on his way, his bare back disappearing out of the bedroom. She heard him in the galley, opening the refrigerator door, closing it. He returned, a dark-green bottle in his hand.

He held it up and sat down beside her. A white towel covered the neck of the bottle. "Champagne—to celebrate our engagement." Efficiently, with the skill of long practice, he released the wire opener and popped the cork into the towel.

"You didn't bring any glasses."

He smiled again, that same darkly wicked smile. "I know."

She thought he meant to give her a sip and made a movement to raise herself partially upright. With one warm hand he pressed her back against the pillow. "No," he said, the gleam of dark amusement echoing the smile on his lips. "Don't get up. It isn't necessary." He lifted the bottle, and before she could dodge away he tilted it, liberally dousing her breasts, her hips, her thighs. The splash of icy liquid on her heated skin brought a cry to her lips.

"Ross!" Her protest was half amusement, half nervousness. This sensual man who combined playfulness with his lovemaking was a new, delicious sensation. For the first time in her life she was glad the years had intervened. He was an adult man making love to her as an adult woman, pleasuring her in ways he would never have considered sharing with his young love all those years ago.

Then he bent his head, his dark hair tickling her skin. A little shiver coursed over her, but that erotic brush of silky hair was only a preview of the delights in store. His tongue found her, moved sensually over her skin, to sip away the champagne and taste the very essense of her. Erotically licking her, covering her damp breasts with slow, exquisitely precise attention, he played artfully over her sensitized nipple, ravaging the taut peak, returning to it again and again, until not a drop of champagne remained. Her skin cooled with evaporation, but the heat his tongue aroused in some dark core of her made her nerves burn with awareness of him in every cell in her body. *Ross,* her mind cried. *Oh, Ross!* She writhed and arched, a captive under his seeking mouth.

In a husky, amused whisper he mocked, "A jug of wine—and thou, my friend."

Laughter mingled with and heightened the passion. "I don't think it was meant quite so literally." She raised up on an elbow in an attempt to escape his plundering tongue, but he seized her arms and pressed her back against the bed, a gleam in his eyes. "Just for that, woman—"

He bent and administered her punishment, his mouth on her damp navel. He gave it the same loving attention he had lavished on her breasts, the pleasing roughness of his tongue swirling erotically in the small circle.

The fire within her blazed white-hot. Her hands clutched at his back; her mind whirled in a marvelous mixture of memory and sensual pleasure. Her eyes closed, then flew open as his mouth moved lower, seeking, seeking. . . .

Knowing that he was vulnerable to her and glorying in it, she made a small sound, as if she were in pain. He eased away from her at once.

"What's the matter? Did I hurt you?"

"Just lie down beside me for a moment."

He frowned, his brows pulled together in concern for her. "Anne, what is it?"

She grabbed at the bottle. He moved to stop her but it was too late. Realizing at once the trap he had been lured into, he growled, "You little witch," but when her hands captured his shoulders, and pushed him down, he lay back unresistingly, his only resistance the guarded watchfulness in his eyes. "Sauce for the gander, I take it." His slow drawl was accompanied by a roguish grin.

She laughed, delighted by the witticism, and he laughed with her, the husky sound of amusement a pleasure to her ears. "Yes," she whispered, leaning forward to brush her lips lightly over his mouth while she held the bottle safely out of his reach. "Definitely sauce for the gander."

His gray eyes turned a deeper silver. "Well? What are you

waiting for?" He was at once challenging and suppliant as he lay stretched before her in all his male beauty, giving her tacit permission to do with his lean body whatever she wanted to do. His willingness to submit to her lovemaking, to take love as well as give it, made her bones melt with the emotion she felt for him. With a thudding heart she gripped the neck of the cool bottle and deftly poured a thin stream of the golden liquid over his chest and taut abdomen. Tiny droplets pooled in the dark mat of hair and glistened in the soft light like diamonds. He couldn't control a gasp. "My God. You were right. It is cold." Then he smiled up at her. "Warm me, honey."

His husky, erotic words sent a shiver of anticipation feathering along her skin. She arched over him and began to caress him with her tongue slowly, infusing her love and desire for him in every stroke. The scent of the wine combined with the musky enticement of his skin made a warm aphrodisiacal perfume that filled her nose. Every inch of him was hers to love and caress— the flat leaness of his stomach, the wide length of his shoulders— and she gloried in the liberty he had given her to explore his body. When her mouth moved lower, he groaned, "My God, you're driving me out of my mind. . . ."

He gripped her shoulders and rolled over, taking her with him. She laughed up at him, wildly exultant. "Too much sauce for the gander?"

He growled softly and took her lip between his teeth, gently tugging at it. The feel of his heavy body against hers filled her with heat; the nudge of his legs between her thighs sent frenzied joy burning through her. The tantalizing teasing of her lips ended. He kissed her, his mouth hard and possessive, his tongue plunging deeply into her mouth. She tasted the heady mixture of wine and Ross and shivered with anticipation. In an endless moment his body hovered above her on the brink of joining with hers. He looked down at her. His eyes glowed with warmth and desire—and love. "Don't ever leave me," he murmured. "I couldn't bear to lose you again."

His husky voice claimed her, and his maleness took her. A searing excitement began to spiral within her, and a heated fever as old as time and yet brand new made her clutch his back and cry out his name. He began to move, and she was lost to the world, her body flung with his to the outer reaches of the universe, where, in a bright and burning heaven, stars burned hotter and hotter until their starry essence exploded in flaming bursts of glory. . . .

He refused to let her go back to the house that evening. "No," he said, "everyone will know tomorrow anyway. You're staying here with me." She didn't argue. She sighed and snuggled closer, the joy of sleeping in the warm haven of his arms too heady to make her consider raising a serious protest.

When they returned the next morning and told everyone their news, Leora was ecstatic. She insisted on turning dinner into a festive occasion. The party was made complete with a bottle of champagne, and when his father popped the cork, Ross's eyes glittered silver and slid down the length of Anne's body with such lazy sensuality that she could almost feel his lips and tongue touching her skin. The thought of what they had shared—and would share again—warmed her body to the tips of her toes.

While she was struggling to regain her composure the wine was poured, and glasses raised. "To the happy couple," her mother said, her face shining with happiness. Anne sipped from her glass, but as she lowered it to the table, she caught Carson Leyton studying her once again, even more severely than he had the previous night. Her head reeled in a sudden, sickening lurch. Did he think she wasn't suitable for his son?

She had an opportunity to find out more quickly than she thought she would. When they had eaten, and the others walked ahead to the music room, she found herself alone with Carson.

"Let the others amuse themselves for a minute or two, Anne. I'd like to talk to you. Would you come into the living room with me?"

186

Her heart raced. She longed for the protective warmth of Ross's presence, the dark flare of love in his eyes. But Ross had walked ahead with Leora, and she was left alone with his father. It could only be that their engagement had displeased him. He had hidden his acrimony from her mother. But now, alone with Anne, he meant to tell her why she couldn't marry his son.

Her stomach knotted. She swallowed the bile that had collected in her throat and said, "Yes, of course." But her mind screamed denial. *No. No. Don't let this happen to me—not again.*

He wheeled into the room ahead of her and turned to face her. She wondered if she would always see this scene in her mind's eye as the evening her dreams had been killed forever and irrevocably, the sun slanting in the window, making long patterns on the wood floor, the leather chairs and couches that were comfortable and well-used, the books that sat in random fashion on the wall shelves.

"Please, do see sit down. There, on the couch, where I can see you."

Once she had done so, Carson Leyton didn't hesitate. "I think I know my son rather well," he began, and the knot in her stomach tied itself tighter, "and I'm almost certain that he hasn't told you the entire story of what happened on that October day ten years ago."

Stunned, her brain whirled, trying to take in his words. They were too remote from what she had expected. "He told me that he didn't receive my message—and that he had gone on a trip and got into trouble."

"And that's all he said?" Eyes a shade lighter than Ross's watched her closely.

"Yes. He asked me to trust him—and I have."

Carson Leyton's shoulders moved upward in a heavy sigh. "I suppose what he did was right, but I—I've had your unhappiness on my conscience for far too long."

"My unhappiness . . ." she echoed, not following him.

"Yes. You see"—he gazed at her, his eyes grave—"I was the one who kept Ross from receiving your message that day."

She paled. "You? But how—"

His slight smile told her he understood her puzzlement. "I simply collected Ross's secretary's memo—and instructed her to say nothing to him about it. I told him you were a woman he wanted to be rid of."

"But—why?"

"Because," he said simply, his eyes locked with hers, "it was a matter of choice. If you came to Ross, I lost Leora."

"I don't understand. . . ."

Carson Leyton's eyes narrowed. "Don't you? Think for a moment. Suppose you were a man who was losing your wife to another man. But you had two beautiful daughters whom she adored. What would you do?"

She thought for a moment—and suddenly she knew. She knew why her father had been so anxious for this reunion to take place. He had been the cause of the separation. "Insist that the children stay with me and deny visiting rights," she said flatly.

"Exactly." Leyton leaned back in the chair, a satisfied smile on his face. "Your father didn't love your mother, Anne. They hadn't really communicated for years. But your father didn't want to admit to failure. He didn't want to let your mother go. And, of course, we were foolish enough and loved each other enough to be seen together long before your mother went to your father and asked for a divorce. He had all the winning cards—and he played them. He insisted that you and Shari stay with him." Leyton paused and then said slowly, "Please understand that I hold no grudge against your father now. Too many years have gone by, and he, too, has his conscience to live with. He knows that he played his part in keeping you and Ross apart, just as I did." Again the pause, as if he were framing the words to make sure they were correct. "Owen threatened to contest the divorce and splash the news of our affair on the front page of every newspaper from New York to California if Ross tried to see you or contact you. At that time the conglomerate was one of the few large ones emerging, and anything I did was news. Leora would have fought even that, but she couldn't bear to involve you. She knew the scandal would hardly touch Shari, but it would harm you very much, and damage your chance of a career."

He gazed at her. "You were very young. We all thought we were doing what was best for you at the time. But we were wrong, weren't we? Can you forgive us—all of us?"

He was not a man to plead, but she was not proof to the imploring tone. And if she faced the truth, she realized that marriage to Ross now, with the years of college and teaching and experience of working with people, was infinitely better than being thrown into his high-tension world at the age of eighteen.

Impulsively she got to her feet and walked to her future father-in-law. "There's really nothing to forgive, you know. Because if it hadn't been for your love for my mother, I might never have known Ross." She leaned over and hugged his broad shoulders.

"I'll give you the greatest compliment I can give any woman, Anne. You're very like your mother." He grasped her arm and held her close. "When I had the stroke that confined me to my bed and nearly made me a vegetable, I offered her the opportunity to walk away. She wouldn't go. She stayed with me, goading me into the therapy sessions. She's brought me this far—and there's a possibility I may be walking again soon."

"I'm very glad." Her eyes filled.

"And I'm glad to welcome you into this family."

"Is this a private hug-in—or can anyone join?" Ross leaned against the doorframe, watching them, his dark eyes playing over his father and his fiancée with a rueful, knowing look. A surge of love for him overwhelmed her. He had refused to tell her everything because he hadn't wanted her to despise her father. But Carson Leyton had told her the truth in a way that made it impossible for her to bear a grudge against her father— or against himself. He had told the story with a compassionate understanding of all the people involved, and he had earned her everlasting love and respect because of it.

"You're always welcome to hug my favorite daughter-in-law, Son."

"Father, you're generous beyond measure" was the dry answer.

Ross didn't move toward her then, but a week later, the day after they were married, when they lay together out on Anne's sun deck, he leaned over her already-sun-kissed body and untied the strings of her bikini top. "Mrs. Leyton, you have entirely too many garments on."

"Mr. Leyton, you're getting repetitious. That's the same thing you said last night." She laughed up at his dark face.

He nuzzled her smooth breasts, which his probing fingers had freed. "If that means you want me to stop undressing you—"

He withdrew his hand and sat up. She made a small sound of protest and clasped her hand around his neck to bring his head down to her mouth.

After a long, satisfying kiss, she pushed him away and said in a serious tone, "Ross, darling, can you really move to Runford temporarily—without jeopardizing yours and your father's investments in the conglomerate?"

His smile was wicked. "My dear, with you beside me, I can do anything."

"And you really don't mind locating in Runford for the rest of the winter—and financing Dina's musical training when we do leave?"

"I really don't mind, love. It was my suggestion, remember? Umm, let me taste you again. Coconut, today, are we? Or just— nut?"

She aimed a mock swipe at him, all too aware that his fingers were busy at the strings of the tiny strip of material she wore on her hips. "I must be a nut to agree to sunbathe with you, Ross, stop it."

He was unmoved and stripped the last remaining barrier to his

190

admiring eyes away. "You don't want to go back to New York with unsightly tan lines, do you?"

"Under all those winter clothes—who will notice?"

"I will," he said, and stopped the discussion by closing her mouth with his own.

LOOK FOR NEXT MONTH'S
CANDLELIGHT ECSTASY ROMANCES ®